Antarctica:
Wilderness at risk

The 100-metre high face of the Barne Glacier dwarfs a Sno-Trak parked on summer sea ice. Many of Antarctica's glaciers terminate offshore as "ice tongues", floating on the sea but buffered by permanent sea ice. *Mike Bradstock*

Antarctica:
Wilderness at risk

Barney Brewster

Friends of the Earth

Published in the United States
by Friends of the Earth Books
1045 Sansome, San Francisco
California 94111

LO-913890-51-0

Library of Congress Catalog Card Number 82-70159

Typeset by Computype Services Ltd, Wellington, New Zealand
Printed in Hong Kong by Wing King Tong Co., Ltd

CONTENTS

ACKNOWLEDGEMENTS

I would particularly like to thank Roger Wilson for his invaluable editorial assistance, and others of Friends of the Earth for their help: Angela Bodley, Audrey Dill, John Horrocks, Mike Bradstock, Michael Bland and Mrs Eunice Trussell.

Thanks are also due to Dr Peter Barrett, for his very helpful comments and suggestions, to the photographers for their enthusiastic support, and to Roger who rendered when all else failed. Many others have also contributed to this book in other ways, for which I am again grateful.

Barney Brewster

FOREWORD

Since the seeds of awareness were sown in the 1960s, the environmental movement has faced many challenges. Concerned people the world over have devoted huge amounts of time and energy to the protection of the earth's natural heritage, battling the forces of commercial greed or national prestige. Fortunately, the oceans, forests, mountains and wildlife of this planet all have their champions. For the survival of the human race depends on the preservation of an environment which is capable of supporting it. We are totally dependent on an environment made up of a closely-knit web of plants and animals, all interdependent.

In the past, humankind has shrugged its shoulders, acknowledged this interdependence while smugly continuing to modify the global environment, dooming some species to extinction, and threatening others. In many cases, the effects were, to humankind, scarcely perceptible. In others, the extinction of a species has meant a change in our way of life, but one which we have been able to accommodate.

This cannot, however, continue indefinitely. The human race now exerts far greater control over its environment than it ever has before, and the blunders now being made are much more serious and on a larger scale than the mistakes of the past. Sooner or later, drastic changes over the entire ecosphere will occur because of the arrogance of the human race.

So it is with Antarctica. The fragility of the Southern Ocean ecosystem is compounded by its simplicity; human greed and ignorance have already endangered many of its species. Exploitation of the Antarctic mainland is also fraught with difficulties; there is the real risk, for example, of large-scale exploitation triggering the melting of the Antarctic icecap, or at the least destroying its tremendous value to science.

There can be no justification for the exploitation of Antarctica except in terms of human greed. For we do not *need* Antarctica's supposed resources but merely desire them to give longevity to a way of life which must, ultimately, come to terms with its own bankruptcy. We have to stop somewhere in our quest for more resources, because resources are finite. Should we not stop this rape *before* we destroy the last remaining great wilderness, rather than afterward?

The challenge faced by the environmental movement over the prospective exploitation of Antarctica is without precedent in the history of the movement. It is no longer a species, a forest, or even a range of mountains, that is at risk, but an entire continent.

Friends of the Earth is an international organisation committed to the conservation, restoration, and rational use of the ecosphere. In the context of Antarctica, this can only mean our steadfast opposition to the exploitation of that continent.

National groups of Friends of the Earth in New Zealand, Australia and the United States have been particularly concerned, and have lobbied at the international conferences where the future of Antarctica has been considered.

For the international community intends to "solve" the problem of Antarctica in two stages. The first, completed in 1980, involved the setting up of a Marine Living Resources Convention to regulate the exploitation of the Southern Ocean. The second stage will focus on how Antarctica's mineral wealth might be extracted. Agreement on this issue will be trickier, for there is the complicating factor of sovereignty: the non-recognition by some nations of other nations' claims to Antarctic territory. If there are fortunes to be made in Antarctica, as some believe, then these issues will become paramount.

No mineral resource will cause more tension than oil, which many believe to be present in vast quantities off the coasts of Antarctica. A major and sustained flare-up in the politically troubled Middle East will send the industrial nations scrambling for alternative supplies. Whoever claims Antarctica's oil is likely to be challenged, because any claim to Antarctica's resources is necessarily flimsy in international law.

And the question of Third World participation in the "development" of Antarctica may also have repercussions. Why, some are already asking, should the developed nations, by reason of their greater financial and technological standing, extract economic benefits from Antarctica, furthering the gap between rich and poor nations?

The best interests of the human race will be served by maintaining Antarctica as it is — as a wilderness, essentially uninhabited. This book, in itself, will have little impact on the forces which are at work in seeking to exploit that continent. But no political change (and this *is* a political issue) is possible without a thorough understanding by the public at large of the issues and choices. By commissioning this book we hope that we are making a contribution to that understanding.

Roger Wilson
National Organiser
Friends of the Earth (New Zealand)
Wellington 1981

Mt Erebus, an active volcano, looms 3,794 metres above Antarctica's McMurdo Sound. Open stretches of water occur for about two months each summer in the Sound and the neighbouring Ross Sea; elsewhere the continental coast is ice-locked virtually all year. *Antarctic Division, DSIR*

"There can be no justification for the exploitation of Antarctica, except in terms of human greed. For we do not need Antarctica's supposed resources — we merely desire them to prolong a way of life which must, ultimately, come to terms with its own bankruptcy."

Friends of the Earth (New Zealand)

The Transantarctic Mountains form Antarctica's continental backbone, with peaks as high as 4,800 metres. This scene is of the Darwin Mountains, a transantarctic range in Southern Victoria Land, with Hatherton Glacier in the middle distance. *Antarctic Division, DSIR*

Chapter 1

THE WHITE CONTINENT

Antarctica is the continent of superlatives. Of all the seven continents, it is the most inaccessible and inhospitable — a desert of ice with the coldest, windiest and driest climate in the world.

Although in the distant past it was adjacent to the land masses of South America, Africa and Australia, Antarctica is now 950 kilometres away from the nearest neighbouring land, Cape Horn.

Isolated at the bottom of the world for the last 25 million years, it has had only a tiny, transient human population since the turn of the century. It is only by great effort and expense that humans can survive there at all.

The continent and its ice sheet have a fundamental influence on our planet's oceans and atmosphere, making it a scientific laboratory of enormous importance. Until now, Antarctica's remoteness and forbidding climate have safeguarded its splendour, but our resource-hungry world will not be long in threatening this purity — with possibly catastrophic results.

Continental Antarctica covers 10 per cent of the world's land surface, an area about one and a half times the size of Australia. The surface area of Antarctica varies with the seasonal expansion and retreat of the pack ice. In late winter and spring, pack ice can extend up to 1,100 kilometres from the coast, reaching 60°S in some places, and effectively isolating the continent from access by ship from mid-

March to November. The pack ice has an average thickness of about two metres, and can easily crush unwary ships trapped within it — as several early explorers found to their cost. Except for some areas of fast ice along the coasts, little of the pack ice persists from year to year.

It is the ice sheet which is the central and most striking feature of Antarctica. Formed from the compacted accumulation of about 100,000 years of snow, it covers about 98 per cent of the continent proper. The total volume of ice in Antarctica is a staggering 30 million cubic kilometres, lying in an average thickness of 1,600 metres and constituting 70 per cent of the world's fresh water reserves. The sheer weight of this ice has warped the earth's crust some hundreds of metres downwards, so that much of the actual land mass of Antarctica lies below sea level.

If the ice sheet were somehow removed, the land mass would rise to compensate — as indeed the Scandinavian land mass is still doing today, 10,000 years since the last ice sheet there receded. This compensating process is known to geologists as isostasy. Melting of all the ice, however, would cause the earth's oceans to rise between 45 metres and 90 metres (estimates vary) as well as giving Antarctica an entirely new coastline. East Antarctica would retain much of its present area, except for several sizable gulfs on its

1

Pressure ridges in the sea ice in McMurdo Sound. The ice is crushed by the seaward motion of the McMurdo ice shelf behind; plates of ice collide to produce these ridges. Mt Erebus and a plume of smoke can be seen in the background. *Mike Bradstock*

outer fringe, but West Antarctica would be reduced to an archipelago of scattered mountainous islands.

The ice sheet formed some time between 25 and 42 million years ago, and has in the past been considerably larger. The present ice sheet is actually two separate sheets — the East and West Antarctic Ice Sheets — separated by the Transantarctic Mountains. Both sheets are slowly but continuously on the move. The accumulated snowfalls are gradually changed through the pressure of their own weight into blue glacier ice which, under the strains and stresses of its enormous mass, moves downward and outward from the centre of the continent. As it descends, this extremely cold glacier ice, with an average temperature of -40°C, is slowly warmed by the friction of flow and by the earth's heat, so that the temperature at the base of much of the ice sheet is near -20°C. Under the immense pressure of the overlying ice, the melting point is lowered to -1.5°C, and this temperature is reached in a number of places beneath the deepest parts of the ice sheet. In these areas, lakes under the ice have been detected by radio-echo sounding.

Over much of the polar plateau the ice is 3,000 metres or more deep, but as the ice moves towards the coast it thins out considerably and comes to be shaped by the bedrock topography. In some places the underlying relief gives rise to glaciers that are amongst the largest in the world. They flow to the coast at speeds approaching 840 metres a year. The world's largest glacier, the Lambert, draws from 250,000 square kilometres of ice surrounding the Prince Charles Mountains, south of Mawson Base. It is 400 kilometres long and up to 80 kilometres wide, and forms the big Amery Ice Shelf where it meets the coast.

Permanent ice shelves averaging from 100-200 metres in thickness float in the two deep embayments that interrupt the almost circular shape of the continent, and others have formed in smaller coastal pockets. These shelves make up 10 per cent of Antarctica's "land" area — the Ross Ice Shelf alone is about twice the size of New Zealand. The ice shelves are fed by inland glaciers, but the accumulation of snow on their own surfaces adds to their growth substantially. The ice shelves, too, are on the move, with the three larger ones (Ross, Ronne and Amery) edging towards the sea at speeds of 900-1,300 metres per year. The Little America Station that Admiral Byrd established on the Ross Ice Shelf in the 1930s has since floated out to sea on an iceberg, and the icy grave of Captain Scott and his comrades, who died about 125 kilometres inland on their way back from the South Pole, may now be somewhere near the sea edge. [1]

The ice shelves, and the ice sheet itself as it reaches the coast, are continually discharging icebergs. As the ice shelves are moving at a faster rate than the continental

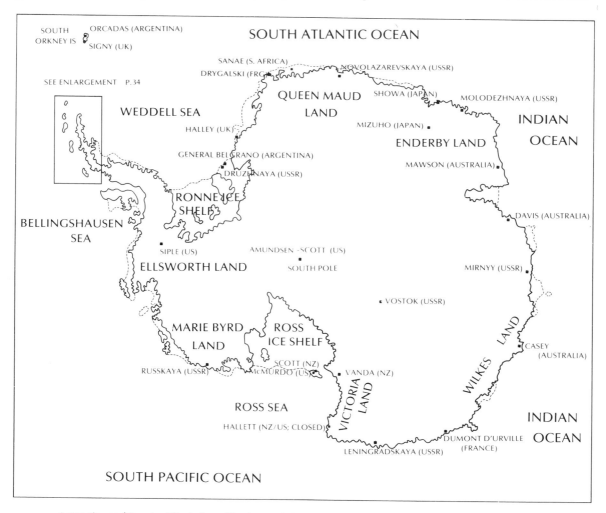

Antarctica and its scientific stations. The Antarctic Treaty of 1959 established the continent as a zone of peace and co-operative scientific endeavour.

ice sheet, they calve a disproportionate share of icebergs — 84 per cent — and also the largest. These are the vast tabular bergs that periodically calve off and eventually move out to sea, where they take some years to melt. Lengths of up to eight kilometres are not unusual, with ice 45 metres above water. The largest berg ever recorded was 335 kilometres by 97 kilometres, with a surface area of 31,000 square kilometres. This was sighted west of Scott Island, north of the Ross Sea, by the USS *Glacier* in November 1956. Unlike their Arctic counterparts, Antarctic icebergs rarely find their way into Southern Hemisphere shipping lanes, although a berg only 48 kilometres off the Cape of Good Hope (South Africa) was seen in 1850.

The combination of the massive ice sheet and the vastness of the surrounding Southern Ocean makes Antarctica a much more inhospitable place than the Arctic. In contrast, the Arctic is a relatively shallow sea with a cover of permanent pack ice some three metres thick, and is virtually surrounded by land. Mean temperatures in the Arctic are 6° to 12°C warmer, with summer maxima of 36°C having been recorded in Arctic Siberia. The flora and fauna of the terrestial Arctic are much richer, and some Greenland Eskimos were apparently bewildered when shown movies of the Antarctic wilderness: "It was a weird world they had seen in these pictures, desolate and pure — quite unlike their living, breathing, hunting, territory". [2] There is a substantial human population living within the Arctic Circle, over two million in fact, with the Russian city of Murmansk alone supporting over 300,000 inhabitants. But only relays of scientists and their support staff live within the Antarctic Circle (66½°S), and their overwintering population is a mere 750.

It is no secret, then, that Antarctica has the worst climate in the world. It presents us with the seeming contradiction of being the world's greatest storehouse of fresh water in a climate that is, on the polar plateau at least, drier than that of the Sahara. On the coasts the mean annual temperature is around -17°C, but further inland much lower temperatures prevail. Remote from the moderating effects of the Southern Ocean, and atop the ice sheet at elevations of 3,000 metres and over, the polar plateau has annual means of between -30° and -55°C. The world's lowest temperature was recorded in August 1960 at the Russian base of Vostok, 1,200 kilometres inland at 3,400 metres above sea level: -88.3°C. At these temperatures steel shatters when dropped and a cup of water explodes into ice when thrown into the open air. At the South Pole itself, at a lower altitude, the highest-ever recorded temperature was -13.6°C in December 1978 — although the pole has a sunnier climate than much of the coast.

These extreme temperatures have their primary cause in the region's low absorption of solar radiation. For up to six months of the year, from March to October, Antarctica has little or no daylight. But despite the six months of night at the South Pole, the total annual radiation received there is about equal to that received in equatorial latitudes. Cloud cover over the polar plateau is minimal, and the great penetration of solar radiation is aided by the thin, dry atmosphere. This works both ways, however, as snow is a very effective reflector of energy. Most of the radiation is reflected back into space by the ice sheet and the sea ice. Sea ice also acts as an insulator over the ocean, contributing to low temperatures inland.

Coastal temperatures are moderated by the ocean and low elevation, although even there summer temperatures rarely rise above freezing, except along the north-western fringe of the Antarctic Peninsula. Dubbed "the banana belt" by Antarcticans, mean summer temperatures along this fringe — outside the Antarctic Circle — remain above freezing for one to four months each year, depending on location. It is possible on the rare, calm, sunny day on the coast to wear light clothes out of doors — until the slightest breeze blows. Even on "the mainland" maximum readings as high as 13°-14°C have been recorded at Lake Vanda and at Davis Station on the Ingrid Christensen Coast (both in 1974). These are spectacular heatwaves by Antarctic standards.

Antarctica is the world's windiest as well as coldest continent, and the winds are a major factor in limiting human activity and comfort there. Great cyclonic storms circle Antarctica in perennial procession from west to east, exchanging atmospheric heat from the Southern Atlantic, Pacific and Indian Oceans with the cold katabatic winds that roll down the ice slopes from the polar plateau. Moist sea air interacting with the cold polar air over the Southern Ocean makes for the roughest seas in the world — the Roaring Forties. The westerly winds blow around the entire circumpolar ocean, unobstructed by land save for the funnelling effect created by the tip of South America and the Antarctic Peninsula. Winds often exceed 200 kilometres per hour. At Mawson's Adelie Land camp, wind velocities in the winter of 1912-13 averaged 64 kilometres per hour for 64 per cent of the time, without a single day of calm.

But few storms bring snowfalls to the interior. Although Antarctica has a reputation for its blizzards, actual precipitation is very low: the blizzards are mainly loose snow being blown around the continent. Snow accumulates in drifts around any surface obstructions, and inland scientific stations have been quickly buried in snow and ice: Byrd Station was completely submerged within five years of its construction in 1957.

At the South Pole it is difficult to measure annual snowfall accurately, as fallen snow cannot be distinguished from blown snow. However, it is thought to be equivalent to less than 25 millimetres of annual rainfall — far less than in most deserts. The coasts are much more humid, and measurable amounts of rain are recorded in summer along East Antarctica and the peninsula. The more southerly coasts of West Antarctica are drier and rain is extremely rare.

Only about two per cent of Antarctica is

In the absence of free-running water, the chief weathering agents of rock are the wind and the stresses induced within the rocks themselves by freezing and thawing. Here, a boulder has been weathered into a cone, while stress patterns can be seen in the distant glacier. *Antarctic Division, DSIR*

free of ice — an area comparable in total to the size of New Zealand. West Antarctica has many isolated peaks, or nunataks, which loom above the ice cover, while mysterious dry valleys, so called for their lack of ice and snow, are found in Southern Victoria Land, not far from Scott Base, and in some other coastal areas in Wilkes Land and in the Vestfold Hills near Davis Station. The dry valleys in Victoria Land are very steep and were carved by glaciers. Fossil shells found high up the Wright Valley, near Lake Vanda, indicate that within the last million years the retreat of the glaciers was followed by an influx of the sea, thus creating fiords.

The dry valleys have several lakes of great scientific interest. All of the lakes are salty — inland seas in effect — although their upper levels can be quite fresh, and while they have permanent covers of ice up to three metres thick, several have bottomwater of unexpected warmth. In the vicinity of Lake Vanda the mean annual temperature is around -20°C, yet the bottomwater at 69 metres is 25°C and is 10 times more salty than the sea. Geothermal heat was at first suggested as a cause, but scientists now favour a solar heating explanation: summer solar energy becomes trapped in the deep layers of high-density salt water. One pond is so saline that it never freezes, even at -50°C.

The dry Wright Valley also has the only river of any size in Antarctica, the Onyx. Arising from a coastal glacier, the Onyx flows inland for 29 kilometres each summer (weather permitting) to Lake Vanda. Each season's flow is recorded at a weir near the lake. Vanda has no outlet, but the summer rise in water level is balanced by the annual evaporation off the lake's ice surface. Other lakes, such as Lake Bonney, are expanding. The delicate balance of sum inflow and annual evaporation means that the levels of the dry valley lakes are very sensitive indicators of climate and climatic change.

The floors of the dry valleys have a surprisingly deep glacial fill, with primitive soils on the surface often showing regular, frost-induced polygonal patterns. These soils share many of the properties of those found by the Mariner probes on Mars, and parallel experiments were carried out on Antarctic and Martian soils. The dry valleys have been termed oases, but one finds few signs of life there. Strangely, there are mummified carcasses — some hundreds of years old — of both seals and penguins distributed throughout the valleys, some as many as 60 kilometres from the coast.

Considering Antarctica's isolation from the rest of the world, the short, cold summers and the dark winters, the high winds and the lack of water, it is no surprise that the land-based flora and fauna are somewhat limited. The only plants able to withstand the extreme conditions of the Antarctic mainland, apart from microscopic soil fungi and algae, are lichens and mosses. These are widespread in the ice-free areas of the continent and on the subantarctic islands.

There are over 500 species of Antarctic lichens, whose ability to grow on inland peaks to within about 500 kilometres of the South Pole thus marks the inner limit of life in Antarctica. The areas around bird rookeries, with their guano deposits aiding moisture and nourishment, are especially favourable environments for lichens, which will cover the rock surfaces with patches of yellow and orange.

Mosses are not as abundant, owing to their greater need for moisture, but there are at least 70 species scattered in sheltered beds in coastal areas, and a few have been found on inland nunataks. A few species of liverworts and toadstools also inhabit the wetter moss beds. In summer months there is the unusual sight in certain coastal places of rosy-hued fields of snow, caused by a species of algae. Other species may form blue-green or bright green patches on ice or damp rocks.

Except for two flowering plant species on the far northern tip of the Antarctic Peninsula, Antarctica certainly has no higher plants such as shrubs, grasses and

Expeditioners rest with a desolate view over the dry Wright Valley in Victoria Land. Carved by glaciers, the dry valleys have since remained free of ice — snow falls rarely and soon evaporates. No one is quite sure why. *Phil Bentley*

herbs. The tree line for the southern region of the world — an isotherm of 10°C annual summer mean, under which trees cannot grow — crosses Tierra del Fuego at mid-point. Even as far north as Campbell Island, 1,900 kilometres from the Antarctic Circle, only a single tree exists — a non-indigenous spruce.

Mites, springtails, lice and midges are the main Antarctic land fauna and they locate themselves as much as possible under rocks. The largest of these is a species of flightless midge, called *belgica,* only three millimetres long. The mites, some species of which have been found as far as 84°S, are the hardiest of these little animals, with a freezing tolerance of -60°C or lower. There are no indigenous vertebrates in Antarctica and no polar bears. Land birds are found on some subantarctic islands far to the north, but there are none on the continent itself.

In great contrast to the poverty of continental life, the Southern Ocean supports a very rich marine ecosystem, and it is from

the ocean that the animal life we so readily associate with Antarctica — the seals and penguins — must take their food. A wealth of microscopic plankton and algae is nourished by the nutrient-rich waters surrounding Antarctica. These micro-organisms are fed on by the zooplankton, which in turn support large populations of fish, penguins, sea birds, seals and whales. These animals are remarkably well adapted to their severe environmental conditions.

One family of Antarctic fish (the Notothenia), for example, has special proteins in its blood which prevent it from freezing in the sub-zero water (depending on salinity, salt water usually freezes at -1.8°C). The ice fish family of the Southern Ocean are the only vertebrates which entirely lack haemoglobin, the red oxygen-carrying pigment in blood, and this also assists survival in such frigid conditions. Without haemoglobin, the viscosity of blood at low temperatures is reduced, as is the energy required to circulate the

7

blood. Other Antarctic fish keep to the ocean depths to avoid contact with ice, for when ice crystals accidentally touch their gills or skin, body fluids begin to freeze and the fish die immediately.

Seals have adapted to the rigours of Southern Ocean life with great success, and a much larger number are found there than in the Arctic. The crabeater seal is the most abundant, and actually accounts for about half the world's total seal population. Despite its name it feeds mainly on krill — small crustaceans which are strained by means of the crabeater's specially modified teeth and palates. The leopard seal is a hunter with much more catholic tastes — penguins, the young of other seals, as well as fish and krill. The relatively rare Ross seal favours squid, but because of its small numbers and preference for heavy consolidated pack ice where few ships can penetrate, little else is known of its habits.

Unlike these pack ice seals, the Weddell seal keeps mainly to the shore ice. It is more gregarious and feeds largely on fish, washed down with some squid. The Weddell seals are very deep divers and have specially adapted eyes for underwater vision in low light levels. They gnaw breathing holes in the fast ice — and ruin their teeth in the process.

Elephant seals and fur seals are also found in the Antarctic, although they are not strictly Antarctic species, breeding as they do on the subantarctic islands. The bull elephant seals are remarkably ugly-looking; they may reach 4.5 metres in length and weigh up to four tonnes, and some have harems of as many as 70 cows. In the nineteenth century, fur seals were almost totally exterminated by fur hunters, but their populations have since recovered to a very healthy size.

The Southern Ocean is also the feeding ground of the baleen whales, which once swam there in great numbers. The blue, fin, sei and minke whales have been savagely reduced by whaling, but fortunately no species has yet become extinct.

The whales feed predominantly on krill, which are strained from the surface waters of the sea through the horny plates — called baleen — that hang from the whales' upper jaws. None of these whales breeds in the Southern Ocean. While in its teeming waters they lay up vast reserves of blubber to sustain them in the less productive but warmer waters further north where they produce their young.

Killer whales also inhabit Antarctic waters and are generally seen in small groups. Killer whales are generalised carnivores and important predators of seals. Herbert Ponting, Shackleton's photographer, had a narrow escape on the sea ice when a killer whale lunged at him from the depths, and Norwegian whalers in the 1920s were astonished to see a pack of killers attacking a blue whale for the sole delicacy of its tongue.

Antarctica has very few species of sea birds — only 41 species even when subantarctic species are included. By comparison, over 120 species breed in the Arctic. However, what they lack in diversity they make up for in number: an estimated 100 million or more birds return to Antarctica each spring to breed around the rocky coastline and on offshore islands. The Adelie penguins are by far the most numerous, but there are three other penguin species, as well as petrels, skuas, gulls and terns. The albatross, the largest and most magnificent of sea birds, breeds on subantarctic islands.

The penguins are the best known of the Antarctic birds and account for 85 per cent of the total bird population. Their little wings have long since given up efforts at flight and are used instead as flippers to propel the birds through the water; on land the penguins waddle, hop or slide along on their stomachs. Penguins spend about half their time at sea, feeding on krill. Their breeding colonies can be exceedingly large, for there are few sections of coast sufficiently free of ice for nesting: some Adelie penguin rookeries have been estimated to contain 250,000 birds. The

Adelie, gentoo and chinstrap penguins reach a height of 60-70 centimetres, but the Emperor penguin is a much larger bird, standing waist high (120 centimetres) and averaging 41 kilograms. The Emperor is unique, for it breeds on the continent over winter. In the appalling cold of winter, and in almost continuous darkness, the male Emperor incubates the egg on its feet on the ice by the coast. Huddling together closely when conditions are especially bad, the males wait for the spring when the chick hatches and the female returns from the open sea, across kilometres of pack ice, to deliver its first meal.

Petrels have found Antarctica to be much to their liking, and 24 species from the petrel family breed there — though only the snow petrel spends all of its life in the Antarctic region. The Antarctic petrel nests in only nine widely scattered colonies, one of which is more than 100 kilometres from the sea. This colony is in the Theron Mountains, inland from the Weddell Coast, and at 72°S it is the most southerly breeding area known for any bird. [3] In the Shackleton Range, another 150 kilometres further south, snow petrels have been sighted, although no nests have been found there.

Skuas and terns mainly scavenge along the shoreline, robbing penguins of their eggs whenever they can, but skuas have even been seen as far south as the pole itself. The Arctic tern spends half the year around the Antarctic pack ice but each austral winter flies 18,000 kilometres back to the Arctic to breed. Some Antarctic sea birds go only as far north as they need to in order to gain open water for feeding, while others move further north into the open ocean. The giant petrels and wandering albatrosses range well into temperate regions. The wandering albatross proved its name when a breeding pair banded at South Georgia were recaptured the next year, still together, at sea off the New South Wales coast.

The Southern Ocean ecosystem is a rich one, but its few species and short food chains also make it a very fragile one, not yet fully understood and deserving of protection.

NOTES

1. *New Zealand Herald,* 19 Nov 79, from *The Times.*
2. Wally Herbert, *A World of Men,* 1968, p.230.
3. Gavin Johnstone, *Habitat,* Jan 1978, p.16.

Chapter 2

THE ADVENT OF MEN

The existence of a great southern continent had been suggested by the ancient Greeks, who reasoned that there must be Terra Australis Incognita to balance the continents in the north. Its huge hypothetical dimensions thus featured on navigators' maps until the eighteenth century.

The Maoris, too, had vague legends of a white land somewhere to the south, and according to Rarotongan legend at least one intrepid Polynesian voyager had been there. About 650 A.D., notes the ethnographer S. Percy Smith, the courageous Ui-te-Rangiora made a very long journey south, and returned with stories of "rocks that grow out of the sea, in the space beyond Rapa (an island on the S.E. fringe of Polynesia); monstrous seas; the female that dwells in the mountainous waves, whose tresses wave about in the waters and on the surface of the sea, and the frozen sea of *pia* (arrowroot) . . . a foggy, misty and dark place not shone on by the sun. Other things are like rocks, whose summits pierce the skies; they are completely bare and without any vegetation on them." [1]

The Tongans also cherish some traditions of the ice-covered ocean, which they call *Tai-fatu* (meaning the thick, fat-like or congealed ocean), to which some of their ancestors had once been in far-off times. The Polynesians were very daring and skilful navigators, and many early European explorers remarked on their eagerness to travel and on the prestige associated with it. Their canoes were certainly seaworthy — up to 50 metres long and either doubled or outrigged for stability. But it seems strange that descriptions of cold do not appear in this account — one would surely expect them as the very first comment from seafarers from tropical lands.

Dr David Lewis who, in 1972-73, made the first single-handed voyage to the Antarctic, has thrown cold water on the plausibility of a Polynesian excursion to the Southern Ocean: "Legends to the contrary, scantily clad men in semi-open boats, even seamen of the calibre of the Maoris, could never have survived in the far south." [2] Lewis' own vessel, the 10-metre sloop *Ice Bird*, was in fact thrice capsized and twice dismasted on his voyage to the Antarctic. Additionally, he points out that the legends were recorded very late — Smith recorded his Rarotongan account in 1897 — when Maoris had already served on European ships in Antarctic waters. Wilkes' 1840 expedition had had at least one Maori sailor on board. [3]

The European exploration of the great southern continent was slow and halting. In the fifteenth and sixteenth centuries, the epic voyages of discovery by European navigators had enabled cartographers to sketch in the coasts of Africa, much of Asia and the Americas, but further south they were left guessing. A map made by William Blaeu soon after Magellan's circumnavigation (1519-22) shows the shores of North Australia, New Guinea and Tierra del Fuego joined in one single continent. When Tasman skirted the west coast of New Zealand in 1642, he took it to be a promontory of Terra Australis Incognita. He named it Staten Landt because that name had been given to land discovered east of Tierra del Fuego in 1616, and he thought New Zealand to be part of the same great continent.

In the eighteenth century a few explorers risked the stormy southern seas in search of the riches which they believed must surely abound in the mythical land, but when its first sentinel in the southern Indian Ocean was discovered in 1739 there was complete disappointment. Bouvet Island — the remotest in the world — was over 2,000 kilometres from anywhere; a precipitous and totally desolate island capped with ice, and with seas so rough that even with a fortnight's tacking its first discoverers could not approach close enough for a landing. There was land further south, for sure, as rock debris could be seen on icebergs drifting north, but it remained for Captain James Cook to establish that its geography was confined to the south polar region.

Cook was the first authenticated Antarctic explorer. He circumnavigated the continent on his voyage of 1772-75, and was the first to cross the Antarctic Circle. Probing further south at several points, he was turned back each time by heavy pack ice. Thus he was not able to sight the mainland, although at his southernmost point, 71°S, he was only 165 kilometres north-west of Thurston Island. The rigours of the south, and its icy desolation, convinced Cook that "the world would not be benefited by ... a country doomed by Nature never once to feel the warmth of the Sun's rays, but to be forever buried under everlasting snow and ice."

The voyages of the Russian Thaddeus Bellingshausen, in 1819-21, narrowed even further the field in which an antarctic continent might be found. He surveyed the South Sandwich Islands and discovered that they were not a northern extremity of the southern continent as had been supposed. Like Cook, Bellingshausen sailed right around Antarctica without sighting the mainland, although at his most southerly point, 69°S, he was only 85 kilometres from the coast of Queen Maud Land.

Sealers had been attracted to the South Atlantic subantarctic islands by Cook's reports of great seal stocks and in this period they began to make important discoveries of their own in the vicinity of the Antarctic Peninsula. William Smith discovered the South Shetland Islands, not far from the northern tip of the peninsula, when in 1819 he sailed further south from Cape Horn than usual to avoid a particularly bad gale.

There is some controversy over who was first to sight the Antarctic Peninsula, the main contenders being the sealers, Nathaniel Palmer (USA), and Edward Bransfield (UK), both in 1820. Another sealer, John Davis, became in 1821 the first to land on the peninsula and others made further discoveries as they moved southwards in search of new seal colonies to devastate. Enderby Brothers, an English whaling and sealing company, sent several small ships along the continental coast in the 1830s, and in 1839 Captain John Balleny made the first landing south of the Antarctic Circle, on the islands that bear his name some 2,200 kilometres due south of New Zealand.

It was in this period, too, that the first national expeditions of a scientific intent were made to the Antarctic region. The investigation of the earth's magnetic field was an important scientific issue at the time, and inspired by the theories of the famous German mathematician, Karl G. Gauss, separate expeditions by the French (D'Urville), the Americans (Wilkes) and the British (Ross) searched for the South Magnetic Pole. Though none of them located it, each made other important discoveries. D'Urville explored the Adelie coast, and named it, and the penguins, after his wife. Wilkes' expedition of 1839-40 was the largest yet organised, and on a lengthy cruise his six ships mapped the eastward coast which was later to be given Wilkes' name. Turned north by ice conditions, Wilkes and his scientists eventually sailed to New Zealand. They spent some time in the Bay of Islands, and had some disparaging comments to make both on the infant European settlement there, and on the Treaty of Waitangi, which had just been negotiated with the Maori chiefs. [4]

The British expedition under James Clark Ross of 1840-43 was much better prepared for work in polar waters than were those of D'Urville and Wilkes. His two vessels, *Erebus* and *Terror*, had been specially strengthened for ice conditions by the installation of double decks, double

shore island and formally claimed the new lands for Britain.

Antarctica's existence as a continent was, however, still unproved — Ross was of the prophetic opinion that the ice rested on a polar archipelago. After his expedition there was a lull of 50 years in which Antarctica received little attention and later exploration was undertaken mainly by steam ship. (Ross's two ships were fitted with engines and propellors on their return to England in preparation for an Arctic mission). Polar exploration over the next 50 years was focused on the more accessible and promising Arctic, with Antarctic activities confined to the oceanographic cruise of the *Challenger* (1872-75) and a private German expedition to the western Antarctic Peninsula in 1873.

Scientific interest in the poles gathered momentum with the First International Polar Year of 1881-82, but only two

The first Antarctic explorers to break through the sea ice to open water in the Ross Sea were astounded to encounter "the Great Ice Barrier". Now known as the Ross Ice Shelf, its ice cliffs extend some 1,300 kilometres across the Ross Sea embayment. Scott's ships are here shown berthed against the sea ice.
Canterbury Museum

hulls, water-tight compartments and reinforcing beams. Ross was already experienced in polar work, having previously made a four-year voyage to the Arctic, where he had located the North Magnetic Pole in 1831.

In 1841 his Antarctic expedition successfully penetrated the pack ice and reached the open water of the Ross Sea, where the next month was spent sailing along the coast of Victoria Land and the edge of the formidable "Ice Barrier" (Ross Ice shelf). Ross made a landing on an off-

scientific stations were set up south of the equator, and neither was in Antarctica itself. Not until the late 1890s did Science establish a foothold on the continent — to herald what is known as the Heroic Age of Antarctic exploration.

At the same time, whaling companies became interested in the potential of the Southern Ocean. The invention of the harpoon gun in 1864 had hastened the slaughter of whale stocks in northern waters, and the gun's inventor, Sven Foyn, was behind several exploratory whaling cruises in Antarctic waters in the 1890s. The search for new whaling grounds led a Norwegian expedition under Henrick Bull to the shores of Victoria Land in 1895. At Cape Adare the first landing on the continent was made at 2 a.m. under the polar sun on 25 January.

A member of this expedition, C.E. Borchgrevink, subsequently organised the first expedition to overwinter on shore. The men camped at Cape Adare from February 1899 to January 1900, and then sailed further east alongside the ice shelf. From the Bay of Whales, a break in the shelf later used by Amundsen in his bid for the South Pole, Borchgrevink and his two Laplander companions mushed dog-sleds south to nearly 79°S. They pioneered in the use of dogs to pull sledges, and left 92 of the huskies on Stewart Island, New Zealand, on their return to civilisation.

Borchgrevink's party had not been the first to experience the gloom of an Antarctic winter. The previous year a Belgian expedition in the ship *Belgica* had become frozen in the sea ice off the western coast of the Antarctic Peninsula. The *Belgica* drifted in the pack ice for nearly a year before release in February 1899. The men found the long polar night particularly depressing and debilitating.

In *Through the First Antarctic Night*, the expedition's doctor, Frederick Cook, describes the great excitement and relief of the men as they watched the first sunrise of the new season: "After so much physical, mental, and moral depression and after having our anticipation raised to a fever heat by the tempting increase of dawn at noon, it is needless to say that we are elated at the expectation of actual daylight once more . . . Every man on board has long chosen a favourite elevation from which to watch the coming sight. Precisely at twelve o'clock a fiery cloud separated, disclosing a bit of the upper rim of the sun . . . For several minutes my companions did not speak. Indeed, we could not at that time have found words with which to express the buoyant feeling of relief, and

the emotion of the new life which was sent coursing through our arteries by the hammerlike beats of our enfeebled hearts." [5]

The two decades which followed saw a multitude of expeditions, each with a different scientific and geographical aim. The Sixth International Geographical Conference in London had called Antarctic exploration "the greatest still to be undertaken", and between 1900 and 1914 there were expeditions from Norway, Sweden, Germany, Britain, Australia, France and Japan. To be sure, their motivations were not entirely scientific. It was the afterglow of the Victorian Age, and chaps still dashed about for King, Queen and Country, pushing back frontiers and staking out claims for far-flung empires. In the new age of rapid communications and the popular press, polar explorers sought the financial backing of the newspaper barons as well as support from the wealthy geographical societies. There was much more than scientific knowledge to be gained — personal and patriotic glories were just as important.

The quest which captured the public imagination with the greatest force was that for the South Pole. Thus the three most famous names in this Heroic Period of Antarctic exploration are Scott, Amundsen and Shackleton.

Robert Falcon Scott led the British Antarctic Expedition of 1901-04. Using their ship *Discovery* as a base — it was frozen-in at McMurdo Sound for two successive winters — Scott and his men reconnoitred the Ross Ice Shelf and the land to the east and west of it. On one of their several dog-sled expeditions across the ice shelf they reached 82°S. This was an advance of over 320 kilometres on Borchgrevink's record, but Scott was appalled at the suffering of his dogs under the extreme conditions.

Air travel of a sort was introduced to Antarctica when Scott used a captive balloon for aerial reconnaissance. He ascended to 245 metres to survey the icy

Captain R. F. Scott, R.N., M.V.O.

Robert Falcon Scott (1868 - 1912), Captain in the Royal Navy. Scott saw polar exploration as a superb means of furthering his career, but although an able scientific investigator and a good writer, his failure to prepare and organise his party properly was a major factor in the tragedy of his second expedition. *Canterbury Museum*

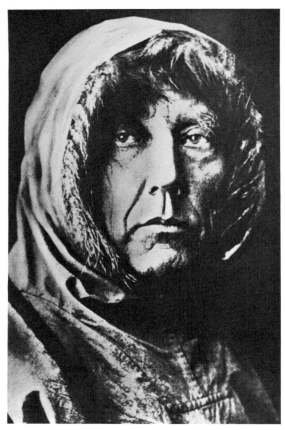

Roald Amundsen (1872-1928), Arctic and Antarctic explorer. Amundsen's main ambition was to be first to the North Pole. Deprived of this honour by Peary in 1909, Amundsen decided to try for glory in the Antarctic. He was a shrewd and careful planner, but his contribution to polar cartography was minimal. *Canterbury Museum*

plain to the south. But the balloon leaked, and a short supply of hydrogen meant this was the only ascent.

Although Scott had no scientific background, he proved to be a competent scientific investigator and a good writer. He was promoted to Captain on his return to England in 1904, and was later to lead a more ambitious expedition.

Thousands of kilometres to the east, the first permanent base in the Antarctic region was established. In 1903 a Scottish expedition, unable to penetrate the ice of the Weddell Sea, had been forced to retreat to the South Orkney Islands, and had

built a meteorological station there, on Laurie Island. This was handed over to the Argentinians in early 1904, and has been maintained by them ever since.

Ernest Shackleton pioneered the route to the South Pole in 1909. He was in Scott's sortie across the Ross Ice Shelf in 1902, but had become seriously ill with scurvy: much to Shackleton's dismay, Scott had him invalided home. Back in England, however, Shackleton raised funds for his own small expedition.

Shackleton experimented with motor transport, taking with him a specially built 15 h.p. Arrol-Johnston car. This machine

The first aerial reconnaissance in Antarctica. Captain Scott made a single ascent to 245 metres during his first expedition of 1901-04. A few days later, a separate German expedition also used a balloon for aerial surveys some 2,700 kilometres to the east at Gaussberg. *Canterbury Museum*

Below: Scott's huts during the first expedition. Exceptionally favourable summer conditions allowed Scott to dock the *Discovery* immediately offshore from Ross Island. The ship remained there over the two winters of the expedition but was almost abandoned the summer of its departure because of ice conditions. *Canterbury Museum*

had a maximum speed of 25 kilometres per hour, and its two fuel tanks gave it a range of 500 kilometres, but it was not a success. Despite the provision of sledge runners and wooden blocks shod on the wheels, the car proved far too cumbersome on the many different surfaces of ice and snow it encountered. Its happiest days have been spent on display in the Antarctic Wing of the Canterbury Museum in Christchurch, New Zealand. Shackleton also took a printing press and a movie camera to Antarctica and his film added a great deal of interest to the lecture tours he made on his return to England.

Along with three companions and a team of hardy Manchurian ponies, Shackleton set out for the pole, but a shortage of supplies stopped his party when only 175 kilometres from their goal. Time had been lost in the difficult climb to the ice plateau, and the ponies had had to be shot. Still, Shackleton's scientists had made significant discoveries. They located the South Magnetic Pole, and had climbed to the summit of Mt Erebus (3,794 metres).

Back in England, Shackleton became a national hero. The scene was set for the final race to the pole — and for a historical controversy, still alive in the 1980s, over the rival expeditions of Scott and Amundsen.

Until this time, polar explorers seeking their place in history had had either geographic pole to strive for. But in April 1909, Robert Peary and his three Eskimo companions had reached the North Pole by dog sled across the sea ice from Greenland. Though Peary's phenomenal daily distances have since made this achievement open to dispute, the hopes of other polar adventurers were turned to the Antarctic.

Roald Amundsen had set his sights on the North Pole conquest since boyhood. He had been first mate on the *Belgica* in order to gain polar experience, and in 1906 became famous as the first to make the drift through the Arctic North-West Passage from the Pacific to the Atlantic.

15

Amundsen, flying the flags of both science and polar conquest, had been planning another expedition to the Arctic, but he secretly changed his destination to the South Pole after news of Peary's triumph. Sailing from Norway in the *Fram* in August 1910, virtually all his crew — and the rest of the world — believed he was sailing for Bering Strait to begin the voyage through the North-West Passage. The Panama Canal was still under construction, so the necessity of rounding Cape Horn in order to reach the Pacific was considered natural.

Amundsen's scientists were waiting in San Francisco. He left them there, for he did not see the South Pole conquest as a scientific venture. Amundsen has been frequently criticised both for his lack of attention to science on this expedition and for the poor records he made of his polar trek. However, his sole aim was to win the pole and thereby put his fame to work in raising funds for his original plan — the expedition to the North Polar basin.

Scott was in Melbourne, Australia, and about to embark on his second expedition when he received the celebrated tele-

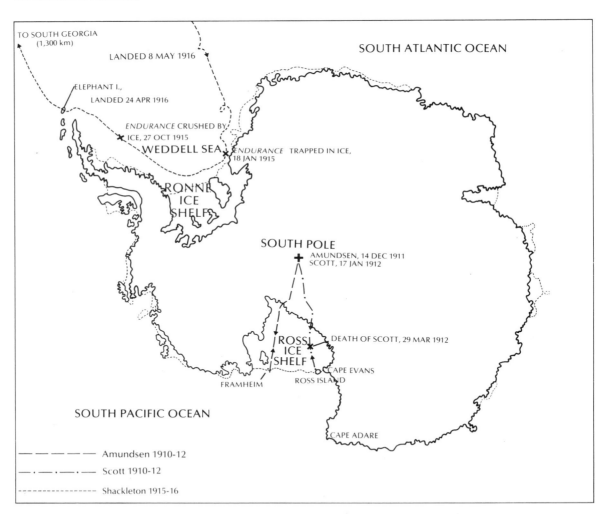

Polar adventurers. From their respective bases at Framheim and Cape Evans, Amundsen and Scott set out in the spring of 1911 on the final dash to the South Pole. Shackleton later attempted to transverse the continent but his ship became completely locked in the Weddell Sea ice with disastrous consequences.

gram: "Beg to inform *Fram* proceeding south. Amundsen".

Both expeditions reached the Ross Sea in January 1911. Amundsen quickly set up his base at the Bay of Whales, and in February had lunch aboard Scott's ship, the *Terra Nova*, while it was still scouting for a mooring.

The contrast between the preparations made by the Norwegian and British parties for the following summer's journey to the pole was marked. With the benefit of historical hindsight, the tragic result of the race to the pole was not surprising. Amundsen's plans were carefully made — his expedition had been well considered and was efficiently carried out. His men were good skiers and experienced icemen. Amundsen took great care of his dogs (though he used them expendably), and he selected men who understood dogs thoroughly.

The *Terra Nova* expedition was very much a naval one, although with a scientific detachment. Two of Scott's men had subscribed to the expedition as volunteers — to the tune of £1,000 each — and Scott himself was rather disorganised. His ideas on transport were disastrous.

Scott had decided on using skis only a few months before departure, despite the fact that his men were not skiers. The expedition had three Wolseley motor sledges but one had gone through the pack ice when offloaded from the ship and had settled in 300 metres of water. The Indian Government sent seven mountain mules, and there were ponies and dogs as well. His experimental mix of transport was quite unsuited to an expedition across the polar plateau.

Scott was so dismayed at the suffering of his dogs on the *Discovery* expedition that he resolved to use them only as a support force. He knew from Shackleton's experience, however, that the different pace of pony and dog made for a difficult combination. Men on skis found it hard to lead ponies, while the latter, in turn, needed snowshoes over soft snow. One of Scott's

scientists had taken a bicycle to Antarctica, but evidently this was not seriously considered a viable part of the South Pole contingent. The remaining two motor sledges also proved to be failures. Eventually, Scott decided that man-hauling the sledges was the noblest means of gaining the pole once the plateau had been reached.

Another contrast between the two parties was in their approach to diet. Amundsen was particularly concerned for the health of his men and was obsessed with the vital need to prevent scurvy, a painful vitamin C deficiency disease. His men spent the winter on a diet of fresh seal meat, wholemeal bread, hot cakes and whortleberry preserve.

Scott, however, was lamentably negligent of his party's diet, in spite of its being common knowledge that a lack of fresh food caused scurvy. There was white bread and an excess of tinned food, both poor in vitamins; seal meat was not served daily, and when offered was overdone in the British tradition. "Fate was sitting at the dinner table." [6]

As Amundsen relied solely on dogs, he was able to set out across the ice shelf on 19 October; Scott had to delay his start until 2 November because the ponies were more sensitive to cold. Amundsen and his four companions — all skilled dog handlers and expert skiers — travelled at a leisurely pace and reached the pole on 14 December 1911. On the journey back they made such good time that, on their return to the *Fram* on 25 January 1912, the crew were too polite to question them, fearing that the expedition must have failed.

The British team, however, was harried by misfortune. Scott even forgot the flag on the outset; from the advance camp he rang the base on the field telephone to ask someone to despatch it. At the foot of the ice sheet the dogs turned back with the last support party, but conditions were too rough for the ponies and they were soon put down. Progress was slow and man-hauling up the face of the ice sheet was

Scott's ponies on the Ross Ice Shelf. They were a special cold-weather breed from Manchuria but were still ill-suited to polar conditions. Shackleton also believed ponies were the best choice in the quest for the Pole: in 1910 he said, "I cannot see how Amundsen can hope to reach the Pole unless he has a large number of ponies on board. He may have dogs but they are not very reliable." Amundsen took over 100 dogs with him and used them very skilfully, though rather expendably. *Canterbury Museum*

extremely arduous. When Scott and his men finally reached the pole to see Amundsen's flag, they were bitterly disappointed. Demoralised and physically weakened, they began the return journey in bad shape. They were short of cooking fuel because although Scott had for some reason decided on a team of five, the cooking pots were designed for four and the food had to be cooked in relays. They were also short of food and their rations were unfortifying. The expedition had only one main cache of supplies, whereas the Norwegians had had three.

When the British pitched their last camp on 19 March 1912, two of the party had already died. The fate of the remaining three, exhausted and half-starved, became certain when a blizzard prevented any further advance to their next depot, only 16 kilometres away. Their bodies were discovered in November 1912 by a search party from McMurdo Sound, where other members of the *Terra Nova* expedition had

Man-hauling on the polar plateau — the most noble way to travel, said Scott, but actually the most arduous. Scott leads on the right; the wheel behind the sledge measures the distance the party has covered. "The frightening risks incurred by Scott's muddle and miscalculation during his last march invited, and one may now say ensured, the ills that overwhelmed it" (Gwyn Jones in the *New York Review of Books*, 17.7.80). *Canterbury Museum*

Sir Douglas Mawson (1882 - 1958) and Admiral Richard Byrd (1888 - 1957), photographed in Wellington in about 1934. Mawson led two expeditions to the Antarctic and Byrd led four. Appropriately, Byrd was also the first to fly over the South Pole. Both men narrowly escaped death in Antarctica: Mawson, starved and poisoned, trudged 140 kilometres on his own across the ice wastes; Byrd nearly died from carbon monoxide poisoning in his solo weather station. *Canterbury Museum*

spent a second winter.

Ironically, the tragedy of Scott assured him and his companions of an enduring place in the history books, and in *Boys' Own*. Many have dismissed Amundsen as an upstart and a bad sport, and have made Scott, for all his bumbling, the gallant hero of the piece.

Shackleton was not to be outdone. In 1914 he set out on a most ambitious — some said foolhardy — project: an Antarctic crossing, from the Weddell Sea to the Ross Sea, via the South Pole. But his transantarctic expedition, though heroic and highly exciting, was a complete failure.

Shackleton's ship, aptly called *Endurance*, became hopelessly trapped in the Weddell pack ice. After nine months it had to be abandoned. The 28 crew then drifted north on the ice floes for over four months, finally making landfall on Elephant Island in the South Shetland group. From there, Shackleton and five of his men somehow survived a two-week voyage in a lifeboat, across 1,300 kilometres of stormy seas to

South Georgia. Landing on its forbidding southern coast, Shackleton and two others made a 36-hour dash across the wintry mountains to the whaling station at Stromness Bay. All 28 of the party were eventually rescued.

As Sir Raymond Priestley, one of Scott's scientists, once remarked: "As a scientific leader give me Scott; for swift and efficient polar travel, Amundsen; but when things are hopeless and there seems no way out, get down on your knees and pray for Shackleton".

None of these Antarctic explorers lived to be old men. Scott was 44 when he died in his tent. Shackleton collapsed and died in 1922 on South Georgia aged 48; he was on his way south for yet another expedition. Amundsen was 56 when in 1928, for all his caution and experience, he gave his life away in an ill-conceived rescue bid for the Arctic airship adventurer Umberto Nobile.

Theirs was not the sole heroism of the age. The Australian expedition of 1911-14 to the George V Coast was noted not only for its important scientific work, but also for the harrowing experience which the leader, Douglas Mawson, was fortunate to survive. With Ninnis and Mertz, Mawson had explored a vast area of unknown territory when Ninnis and the food sledge disappeared down a crevasse. On the trek back, Mawson and Mertz were forced to eat their dogs, and unwittingly poisoned themselves on the husky livers. Vitamin A in sufficient excess is lethal, and there is normally enough in a single husky liver to provide 10 toxic doses for an adult man. After Mertz's terrible death, Mawson spent a month dragging himself the 140 kilometres back to camp.

World War I ended Antarctic exploration for a time, but from 1923 on, oceanographic and biological cruises to Antarctic waters were made by the United Kingdom on 13 successive summers, using Scott's old ship *Discovery*. These voyages were of great scientific value and produced a wealth of information on the

Shackleton's stores as they remain today. The hay bales, provisions boxes and husky kennels lying outside the hut date from the 1907-09 British Antarctic Expedition. The hut is adjacent to a large Adelie penguin rookery at Cape Royds on Ross Island, about 42 kilometres north of Scott Base. *Mike Bradstock*

"The Floyd Bennett", the first aircraft to fly over the South Pole, photographed during tests in Canada. The Ford trimotored plane was named after Byrd's co-pilot on the first flight to the North Pole in 1926. With Bernt Balchen, Harold June and Ashley McKinley, Byrd took nearly 10 hours to reach the South Pole from his Little America base on the Ross Ice Shelf in November 1929. *Canterbury Museum*

nature of the Southern Ocean and its marine life: 25,000 seawater samples came back to the British Museum!

The 1920s also ushered in the Mechanical Age of Antarctic discovery. The American Richard E. Byrd introduced the systematic use of aircraft and aerial photography. Mawson had intended to experiment with aviation during his 1911-14 expedition, but his plane lost its wings in a mishap before departure, and the fuselage was taken down for use as a tractor. In 1928 another Australian, Hubert Wilkins, made the first flight in Antarctica, from Deception Island across the Antarctic Peninsula.

Byrd's first expedition — he was to lead four others — was a private one, sponsored to a large extent by such wealthy men as Edsel Ford and John D. Rockefeller. The names of these patrons now figure on Antarctic maps. Byrd had established his credentials as an explorer with his flight over the North Pole in 1926, and had advised Charles Lindbergh on navigational training prior to Lindbergh's solo transatlantic flight in 1927.

From his base at Little America on the Ross Ice Shelf, Byrd took nearly 10 hours to make the first flight to the South Pole in 1929. There was nothing there "but the fancy of men", Byrd wrote later. "One gets there, and that is about all there is for the telling. It is the effort to get there which counts."

Although Antarctic flying was often severely limited by weather conditions, this was more than offset by the distances that could be covered, the perspective on the terrain that altitude allowed and the usefulness of aerial photographs for map making. Since Byrd, aircraft have been crucial to the making of a detailed geography of the continent.

The Byrd expeditions made other mechanical innovations. Two-way radio communication with the outside world became a feature of Antarctic exploration (Mawson had only managed erratic one-way messages to Australia via Macquarie Island). For his 1934-35 expedition Byrd used tracked vehicles for the first time, and also the autogiro, a precursor of the helicopter. This expedition was also unique for the three cows taken along; their names, unfortunately, have not been recorded for posterity.

The 1930s also marked the advent of women in Antarctica, though their presence is only now becoming properly asserted. Mrs Mikkellson, the wife of a whaling captain, was the first woman to land on the continent: in February 1935 she stepped ashore by the Vestfold Hills, not far from the present Davis Station. Edith Ronne and Jennie Darlington accompanied their husbands on the private Ronne expedition of 1947-48, and were the first women to winter in Antarctica.

Only in the last decade have women been given any place in the field of Antarctic research, in the face of entrenched opposition from those who have preferred to see Antarctica as a macho Last Frontier. When in 1957 two stewardesses from a trial Pan American flight to McMurdo visited the American base to judge a beard-growing contest a large number of men boycotted the event in protest.

NOTES

1. S. Percy Smith, *Hawaiki* 1921, p.175. Although Smith's scholarship is no longer highly regarded, this account is still worthy of note.
2. Dr David Lewis, *Solo*, 1979, p.15.
3. L.B. Quartermain, *New Zealand and the Antarctic*, 1971, p.5.
4. Wilkes describes the Bay of Islands as "anything but picturesque"; its main settlement was "chiefly inhabited by the lowest order of vagabonds . . . [and] appropriately named Blackguard Beach." The Treaty he calls "this act of usurpation". See Quartermain (3) above.
5. See F.A. Cook, *Through the First Antarctic Night*, 1900.
6. See Roland Huntford, *Scott and Amundsen*, 1977.

Chapter 3

THE POLITICAL STAKEOUT

In the black comedy of international politics, Antarctica did not become particularly significant until the 1930s and 1940s, although several formal territorial claims were made before then.

Even in the nineteenth century, explorers had been careful to raise their national flags wherever possible. Ross did this on Possession Island in 1841. A year earlier, D'Urville had made the same symbolic gesture on another island off the coast of Adelie Land. For this ceremony, D'Urville records, a bottle of Bordeaux wine was enlisted, and we are informed that "this generous liquor reacted with advantage against the rigours of the temperature".

Although the continent was seen to be patently useless from a commercial point of view, its strategic possibilities were considered even then. In proclaiming Adelie Land as French territory, D'Urville made the point that "there is at least the advantage that it will never raise up war against our country". The penguins were obviously friendly.

Borchgrevink raised the British flag at Cape Adare in 1899. On his 1908-09 expedition, Shackleton was appointed a postmaster, and specially overprinted New Zealand stamps bearing the inscription "King Edward VII Land" were issued to him. As an administrative act, the issuing of stamps has been commonly regarded as an indication of political possession. Shackleton left stamps in a brass cylinder somewhere on the ice shelf, and at his farthest point south raised the British flag. For Scott's last expedition halfpenny and penny New Zealand stamps were overprinted "Victoria Land".

Formal national claims date from 1908, when the United Kingdom officially declared an Antarctic sector which included South Georgia, the South Orkneys and Shetlands, the South Sandwich Islands and the Antarctic Peninsula. These were made Dependencies of the Falkland Islands, which had been occupied by the British in 1833. The geographical limits set in this official proclamation unintentionally included Tierra del Fuego, which was indisputably South American; so another set was issued in 1917 to clear up the oversight.

These formal claims had their origins in the rise of whaling operations in the area. The Norwegian whaling magnate, C.A. Larsen, had begun modern Antarctic whaling in 1904, but his floating factories required sheltered harbour waters in which to operate. The Norwegians, diplomatically, approached the British for licences. The Falkland Islands Dependencies were established to legitimise the valuable licence fees, and to attempt the regulation of the whale kill within particular limits. Sealing grounds were also mapped and divided into different areas, and licences were applied for.

Above: Looking across the sea ice at New Zealand's Scott Base on Ross Island. In the foreground, expeditioners are preparing sleds. Mt Erebus is just visible in the background. *Colin Monteath*
Below: An unusual scene at the seasonal base at Lake Vanda in the dry valleys region, where heavy snowfalls are a rare event. This photograph was taken after the first fall of snow in about two years. The snow was gone within two hours. *Tony Shaw*

Above: Lake Vanda from atop "The Dias", a peak in the dry valley region. The pale blue ice is permanent cover; the border of darker ice just discernible at the near end melts each summer, forming a moat at the lake margin. *Tony Shaw*

Below: An aerial view of the Lower Wright Glacier at the seaward end of the dry Wright Valley. In the summer, the meltwater from this large, very slow-moving glacier is the main source of the Onyx River which flows 30 kilometres inland to Lake Vanda. *Tony Shaw*

In 1888, at a Berlin conference called to legitimise the colonial carve-up of Africa, the European powers had agreed that effective occupation should be the main basis of sovereign claims, although some rights of discovery were also conceded. Accordingly, the British consolidated their claim with the exercise of bureaucratic authority in the area. British magistrates were resident on South Georgia from 1909, and on Deception Island (off the tip of the peninsula) each summer from 1910 till 1930. Customs and whaling officers also made appropriate moves wherever whaling activities were based. In the 1920s, the development of larger factory ships with slipways meant that neither the shore stations, nor the annual licence payments that went with them, were necessary. Thus only the station on South Georgia continued after 1930.

As whale stocks became depleted in the peninsula area, the whaling companies became interested in the untapped potential of other areas. Whales had been frequently sighted in the Ross Sea, al-

though Bull's exploratory cruise there in 1895 had caught only one — the ship was not equipped to catch the fast-moving whales.

In 1923, with licence applications at hand, the British made the formal announcement of their claim to the Ross Dependency, based on discoveries by Ross in 1841, and by Scott and Shackleton between 1901 and 1912. The Dependency's administration was entrusted to the New Zealand Governor-General, and the New Zealand claim dates from the accompanying Order-in-Council.

The New Zealand Government, at that time unfamiliar with the by-ways of foreign policy, woke up to find itself in charge of a huge slice of the Antarctic. Nevertheless, it was assured by London that no great costs would be incurred. In fact, the New Zealand Government benefited by several thousand pounds a year in licence fees up until 1928. Thereafter, the whaling companies operated from the high seas.

In these first decades of the twentieth century, British as well as other politicians were still struck with the quest of empire-building, and Antarctica seemed ripe for annexation or partition. Some influential politicians made no secret within diplomatic circles of their ultimate aim of incorporating the entire continent within the British Empire. Their policy of extending and asserting British control — albeit with caution — featured in Imperial consultations from 1920, and the Imperial Conference of 1926 decided on another expedition to the little-explored regions south of Australia and the Indian Ocean.

The threat was that Norwegian whalers might weaken British claims by new discoveries, declarations of sovereignty and acts indicating administrative control. The knowledge that Norwegian coffers would then benefit from the whaling activities was enough to add a sense of urgency, but disagreements over the financing of the expedition meant that it did not take place until 1929-31. In spite of increased Nor-

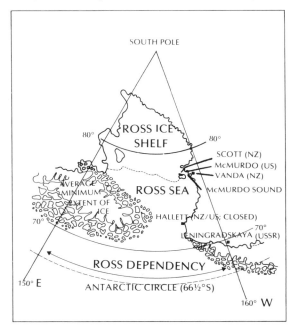

The Ross Sea region, due south of New Zealand. Very little of the Antarctic landmass is encompassed by New Zealand's claim.

wegian activity along the continental coast, the British could not annex the region without further exploration. Thus, while the British-Australian-New Zealand Antarctic expedition (BANZARE), led again by Mawson, was not without scientific justification, its principal objective was a political *veni, vidi, vici*.

The Australian Government was considerably relieved when, in 1933, the British made them the generous endowment of two very large segments of Antarctica. Australian Antarctic Territory consisted of some 6.5 million square kilometres and included nearly half the continental coastline.

The two sectors were cleft by the French claim to the Adelie coast, which had been proclaimed by Presidential Decree in 1924. The French claim was extended inland to the South Pole in 1938, by which time the aerial exploration of the polar plateau by different countries was well under way.

The Germans, with a claim in mind, in that year sent a commercial mapping company to Antarctica. The ship *Schwabenland* was chartered, and was used as a base for an aerial survey of Queen Maud Land. The expedition was a short one — only three weeks — but in six and a half days of flying, 600,000 square kilometres of territory was photographed and reconnoitred; the planes also dropped metal swastikas at intervals of 25 kilometres. The aircraft were carried on the ship and catapaulted from the stern — on a recent visit to New Zealand one of the expedition's photographers, Siegfried Sauter, recalled that "being hurled off the ship over icy polar waters was a hair-raising experience". The aircraft were adapted for the tropics, and their engines frequently misfired. [1]

The Norwegians, concerned that their Queen Maud Land should not become German territory, then proclaimed their formal sovereignty over the area in January 1939. Norwegian explorers had been active in the area and Norwegian whalers had made new discoveries along the coasts from 1929 to 1936. The Norwegian claim has unspecified northern and southern limits and is the only national claim in Antarctica not formulated on a sector basis (moving inwards from the Antarctic perimeter to the South Pole). The use of the sector principle in the Arctic is opposed by Norway, and an Antarctic claim along such lines would prejudice its case in the Arctic, where maritime boundaries between Spitzbergen and Norway are disputed with the Soviet Union.

The American expeditions of the 1930s also had their political motivations. Before his 1939 expedition Admiral Byrd was told by President Roosevelt that he could air drop or deposit in cairns declarations that might help a possible United States sovereignty claim. In 1939 a State Department report to President Roosevelt on the polar regions recommended that the United States take an immediate interest in appropriating a sector of Antarctica, and pointed to the continent's military strategic position, the possibility of transpolar air navigation and the probability of rich mineral deposits. The active political interest expressed by other countries was also an added incentive.

This third American expedition was characterised by Dr Paul Siple, Byrd's second-in-command, as "a colonising expedition". It aimed to establish two permanent United States bases in Antarctica, but with the threat of war with the Japanese in 1941 these were hastily evacuated. The bases were at either side of Marie Byrd Land, the only unclaimed sector of Antarctica and an area extensively surveyed by the American expeditions.

World War II demonstrated the strategic importance of Antarctica for the first time. German commerce raiders based at the subantarctic Kerguelen Islands sank or captured most of the Norwegian whaling fleet, and the control of the Drake Passage between South America and the Antarctic Peninsula became militarily significant. The British presence in the peninsula area

Dome and vent at the South Pole station — with miniature United States flag flying. Snow has drifted in the lee of the prevailing wind and will eventually engulf and bury the structure: this is the fate of all installations on the polar plateau.

lapsed with the more pressing concerns in the north, and the Chileans and Argentinians used this hiatus to their advantage.

After a careful academic investigation, the Chilean Government announced its own claim to the Antarctic Peninsula and associated islands in 1940. It issued a decree "to fix with accuracy the limits of a sovereignty that has existed since the 15th century". This was countered the next year by an Argentinian claim. These claims overlapped both with each other and with the British claim, and marked the beginning of serious political conflict in the region.

The South American claims are based on geographical proximity, geological affinity, effective occupation, and on succession to the original Spanish "rights". Both Chile and Argentina trace their historical rights to a Papal Bull of 1493, when Pope Alexander VI, with considerable largesse, decreed that all lands west of the 46th meridian (and so extending to the South Pole, in a legal sense) be given to Spain.

The Argentinians had never recognised the British occupation of the Falkland Islands — they are still contested — nor would they accept British possession of the islands and peninsula which depended on the Falklands for their administration. Additionally, the Argentinians argued that there had been effective occupation of the South Orkneys since they began operating the weather station there in 1904.

To further their claim, the Argentinians sent a warship to the area, raised their national flag at various points, and left a brass cylinder with a claim sheet inside at Deception Island. This was subsequently returned to the Argentine Embassy in London after the British discovered it the following season. The pro-Nazi stance of the Argentine Government made it highly undesirable, from a British point of view, that the Argentinians should be in a position to control the southern side of Drake Passage. Thus, despite the strains of the war, the British determined to return to the Antarctic in full force, and Operation Tabarin came into being. Bases were built along the peninsula, and the men occupied themselves with survey and scientific work, and with some coast-watching.

The conflict continued in the post-war years, when each summer Chile and Argentina sent their own national expeditions to establish permanent weather stations and conduct photographic reconaissance by air.

Summers in the peninsula area soon became known as the silly season. Base leaders and ships' commanders were under orders to act with extreme dignity, decorum and politeness as hosts to any foreigners who entered "their" territories. As one observer narrated: "It was with the utmost charm and courtesy that the leader of the Argentine base presented his note of protest at the intrusion of the *John Biscoe* into 'Argentine' waters . . . with no less refinement of feeling the British replies were delivered, drawing attention to the confusion of thought on this subject". [2]

But to remove some of the political heat

Ross Island's relative accessibility made it a logical choice for early expeditions and for the American and New Zealand bases established for IGY in 1957. *NZMS 135/Angela Bodley*

the South Americans came to an agreement with the British in 1948 that they would refrain from sending warships to the area in the summers. Still, there were a number of "incidents" as each side disputed possession. These culminated in February 1952 when Argentinians at Hope Bay, at the northern tip of the peninsula, greeted a British party with machine-gun fire. The British made a thoughtful retreat and the Argentine Foreign Ministry later apologised. The following year the British retaliated by deporting an Argentinian party from Deception Island.

Attempts to smooth the waters met with scant success. Both Argentina and Chile declined British invitations in 1947 and 1955 to put the contested claims before the International Court of Justice. The South Americans insisted that their sovereignty, while disputed between themselves, was so clear that no third party could judge this domestic question.

In the post-war years the United States counterbalanced the political equation in Antarctica with expeditions on a massive scale. The Navy's Operation High Jump of 1946-47 was the largest expedition ever mounted in Antarctica, using 13 ships and 4,000 men. From a fleet of 25 planes, about 60 per cent of the continent's coastline was photographed, much of it previously unseen. This expedition, and the smaller one of the next season, was given a secret directive to effect "the extension of United States' sovereignty over the largest possible area of the Antarctic continent". In pursuance of these instructions, the United States Navy erected bronze pipes and buried brass plates. A formal American claim never eventuated, however, as the international situation became too complicated. Nevertheless, Marie Byrd Land has at times been tacitly regarded as an American sector, and as late as the 1960s some maps showed it as such. [3]

Efforts to find an international solution to political developments in the Antarctic began in 1948 when the United States proposed that a small group of countries with Antarctic concerns merge claims and interests to form a condominium — but nothing came of it. This proposal had purposefully excluded the Soviet Union, but in 1950 the Russians made it clear in a diplomatic note that any political settlement of the Antarctic problem must involve their participation. They were not alone in their awareness of the role that Antarctica might play in global political strategies, although the 1946 visit of the Slava whaling fleet had been the first Russian activity in Antarctic waters since Bellinghausen's voyages of 1819-21.

However, with the Korean War came a shift in the focus of international attention, and the settlement of the political question marks over Antarctica was postponed. In 1956 and 1958, however, there were moves in the United Nations to secure an international agreement for Antarctica that would ensure its development for peaceful purposes only. New Zealand's then Prime Minister, Walter Nash, suggested a form of United Nations trusteeship for Antarctica, which would be a "world territory" under United Nations control — but nothing resulted from this proposal either. Few of the other claimant states were in any way keen to relinquish their territorial stakes, be they contested or not.

The increased international interest in Antarctica in the 1950s was matched by a great expansion in scientific work there. The French established a scientific station on the Adelie coast in 1949, and staffed it until 1953. In Queen Maud Land, a joint British-Norwegian-Swedish expedition made meteorological, glaciological and geological observations over the three years from 1949 to 1952. The Australians set up their Mawson Base in Australian Antarctic Territory in 1954, and have occupied it without a break ever since.

The biggest impetus for a political settlement came from the International Geophysical Year (IGY) of 1957-58. Antarctica was singled out for special attention in the IGY, and 12 countries (the seven claimant states plus Belgium, Japan, South Africa, the United States and the Soviet Union) co-operated to implement global scientific research programmes on an unprecedented scale. With this stimulus from science, the human presence on the Antarctic continent burgeoned. More than 40 stations, including New Zealand's Scott Base and Australia's Davis Station, were established south of the 60th parallel.

The IGY heralded the Scientific Age in Antarctic human history, and at its close many diplomats and scientists were anxious that the international co-operation, and the gentlemen's agreement which had shelved all political activity, be sustained.

The Antarctic Treaty, the present international agreement for stewardship of Antarctica, resulted from an American proposal to other IGY participants that they establish an accord to preserve the continent as an international laboratory for scientific research, and to ensure that it was used only for peaceful purposes. With the growing interest of the United Nations in Antarctica, the 12 states were concerned to establish their collective political responsibility there, and by skirting the complicated claims issue they were able to reach an agreement with a speed surprising in international negotiations.

The Treaty was signed in 1959, and came into force in 1961. It stipulates a period of 30 years, after which its terms may be renegotiated.

The main provisions of the Treaty are:
1. Freedom of scientific investigation is to be continued, and scientific plans, observations, results and staff are to be freely exchanged. This objective was considered to be important if Antarctica's value to science was to be fully realised. Scientific co-operation has been genuinely successful among the Treaty nations.
2. Antarctica is to be used "for peaceful purposes only". All military activities, including the testing of weapons, are banned, and there is a system of inspec-

tions to ensure this proviso is maintained. The use of military equipment or personnel is permitted for scientific or logistic purposes. The American (and New Zealand) Antarctic programmes rely on the services of the United States Navy and Air Force, under Operation Deep Freeze, and a New Zealand Army corps undertakes the unloading of supplies at McMurdo Sound each season. Nuclear explosions and the disposal of nuclear waste in Antarctica are also banned.

3. The legal status quo in Antarctica is frozen by the Treaty. Nothing done while the Treaty is in force can be seen to prejudice current territorial claims in their assertion, support or denial of any territorial rights. The Treaty forbids further claims or enlargements of any existing claims. Only by avoiding this very thorny question could a treaty be effective.

4. The Treaty applies to the area south of 60°S latitude, including ice shelves, but not to the areas of high seas, where the rights of international law are given precedence. The Treaty's failure to define how much of the sea is not "high seas" has caused difficulty in later negotiations.

5. Full membership in the Treaty is reserved for the original 12 signatories, and for any acceding state while it conducts substantial scientific activity in Antarctica. "Substantial" is defined in terms of a scientific station or expedition. A country acceding to the Treaty formalises its willingness to abide by the Treaty provisions, but voting and regulatory control are restricted to full or "consultative" members.

Poland acceded in 1961 and became the thirteenth consultative member in 1977 after it had opened a permanent station in the South Shetlands. The West Germans acceded to the Treaty in 1979, and completed construction of a research station on the Ekstrom Ice Shelf in February 1981. They were admitted as the fourteenth consultative member at a meeting of the Treaty powers in Buenos Aires in March 1981.

Other states which have acceded to the Treaty are Czechoslovakia (1962), Denmark (1965), the Netherlands (1967), Romania (1971), East Germany (1974), Brazil (1975) and Bulgaria (1978) and Uruguay (1980). The Netherlands shared the Roi Baudouin Base with Belgium in the late 1950s but has not been active in Antarctic research since. An East German scientific contingent has worked alongside the Russians at Novolazarevskaya intermittently since 1959; East Germany has shown increased interest in the Antarctic in recent years. Brazil, to the alarm of the Chileans, announced its intention to embark on an Antarctic research programme at the time of its accession in 1975, but nothing has been heard of this proposal since.

The Treaty has no secretariat. Instead, biennial consultative meetings are held, with each Treaty nation taking a turn to host the conference. The meetings have been criticised for their lack of open debate — they are closed to the public and the news media. Communiqués, couched in the language of international diplomacy, are issued at each meeting's conclusion.

At the meetings information is exchanged and over 100 recommendations have been adopted, not all of which have been ratified by respective governments. The recommendations cover subjects as diverse as the routing of meteorological traffic to the issuing of anniversary postage stamps, but environmental protection has been a major concern since the early 1970s.

The Treaty nations have tended to operate as an exclusive club, and have consistently resisted all outside initiatives to broaden the stewardship of Antarctica beyond those countries able and willing to invest considerable capital there. Nevertheless, the Antarctic Treaty has been an example of successful international co-operation, aided no doubt by its relatively narrow political base. Its business has been managed with an efficiency that derives from closed plenary sessions and which international bodies with broader constituencies could not hope to rival. The Treaty's emphasis on consensus decision-making has been its great strength in the past, as has the willingness of its members to compromise and co-operate. This is not to say that the Treaty conducts its business at any speed. The most significant agreements under the Treaty take at least six years to push through.

Nor is the Treaty formally equipped to deal with questions arising on Antarctica's resources. The Treaty is silent on such issues for good reason. In 1959 it was feared that negotiations regarding such far-off possibilities would jeopardise the chances for a speedy settlement.

Thus conservation and management regimes have been promulgated and signed outside the legal structure of the Treaty. The Convention for the Conservation of Antarctic Seals — a non-contentious issue — was signed outside the actual Treaty framework in 1972, and on ratification by the majority of Treaty states, came into effect in 1978. The Marine Living Resources Convention signed in Canberra in May 1980 may similarly not be ratified for 10 years. However, like the Agreed Measures for the Conservation of Antarctic Flora and Fauna, they have been accepted as informal guidelines, pending ratification.

A special international scientific organisation plays a very important role as an informal advisory body to the Antarctic Treaty governments. The Scientific Committee on Antarctic Research (SCAR) co-ordinates and exchanges information about scientific activities in Antarctica. Its membership is open only to those countries actively engaged in Antarctic research, and a marine research programme is a minimum requirement for this. The Belgians, though remaining a consultative party to the Treaty, no longer attend SCAR meetings, having closed their Antarctic base in 1962. But other nations involved in Antarctic research — namely Poland, West Germany and East Germany — have gained membership since.

SCAR, which comprises a number of advisory working groups, has instigated a good many Treaty agreements, particularly those of a conservationist nature. Its scientists have developed an international research programme on the biology of the Southern Ocean, the Biological Investigation of Marine Stocks and Systems

A mirror globe at the South Pole enables the photographer to capture himself "at the bottom of the world". Also reflected are the flags of the Antarctic Treaty nations. Amundsen-Scott Station (US) is a few hundred metres away. The exact geographic pole cannot be marked by any permanent fixture because the ice underfoot is forever creeping coastward under its own colossal weight. *Mike Bradstock*

(BIOMASS), and at the request of the consultative parties, SCAR has also produced a preliminary assessment of the environmental impact of mineral exploitation.

It is well to remember that the Treaty has by no means solved the complex question of territorial claims in the Antarctic. These claims, ostensibly shelved for the time being, have continued to be a major headache in international negotiations.

Only five claims (those of France, Norway, Australia, New Zealand and the United Kingdom) are mutually recognised, but as has been shown, the claims of Chile, Argentina and the United Kingdom overlap hopelessly in the Antarctic Peninsula. As well, 17 per cent of Antarctica — Marie Byrd Land and Ellsworth Land — has never been claimed by anyone; both areas are inaccessible even by Antarctic standards.

The other six countries with a presence in the Antarctic (the Soviet Union, Japan, Poland, West Germany, South Africa and the United States) do not recognise any territorial claims, while the Soviet Union and the United States also "reserve their rights".

The official agreement to hold territorial claims in abeyance has not prevented states from pressing their cases as far as they are able through diplomatic channels. The Australians, for instance, are very possessive of their Antarctic territories, and regard them as non-negotiable.

Although Australia's claim dates from an Act of Parliament in 1933 which formally accepted the territories bestowed by Britain, there has recently been a considerable public relations campaign by Canberra to impress on the domestic and international public Australia's "unshakeable" claim to sovereignty in the Antarctic. Yet according to an information paper prepared for the Australian Department of Environment, international legal opinion suggests that there is little chance of the claim's surviving.

The same document declared that Australia has "a bad record" as far as ratification of international Antarctic agreements is concerned. As part of Australia's revitalised commitment to Antarctica, however, the Government was very active in pushing for a marine conservation regime for the Southern Ocean. In 1980, at the final session for the regime in Canberra, the Australians made a concerted effort to ensure that the negotiations were successful.

Australia's rigid adherence to its claim stems from two factors, the first of which is strategic: Antarctica represents the underbelly of Australia. The Australians are mindful of Germany's Antarctic submarine actions in World War II, and although Antarctica is 3,000 kilometres from Australia, it is no greater distance than that which allowed the Japanese to make an excursion into Sydney Harbour from their Pacific theatre of operations in 1942.

In the post-war era, Australia's defence anxieties originate from another quarter. Grenfell Price, an Australian historian, has summed up the significance of Mawson's second Antarctic expedition in this way: "Mawson ranks with Seward and McKenzie and other great Americans and Canadians, who, whether they foresaw the future or not, created the Alaskan and North Canadian barriers between democracy and communism. In an atomic age the unhappy day may come when the lesson of New Guinea may be repeated in the Antarctic, and Australia and the rest of the democratic world may be grateful for the BANZARE voyages." [4]

The Australians have been distinctly nervous at times over the three Russian bases within Australian Antarctic Territory, and the press regularly carries Russian scare stories — generally in the summer silly season when news is short. Nonetheless, one of the main Australian worries is the total lack of "a presence" in their smaller polar slice. The Australian sector between Adelie Land and the Ross Dependency contains only Mawson's deserted camp and a Russian base. With the increasing international salivation over Antarctica's potential resources, it seems likely that an Australian base will be established there within the next decade.

The regard for the mineral potential of the Antarctic is the other factor influencing the Australian position. Speculation over the use of icebergs as a possible freshwater resource for the Australian interior is unlikely to arouse territorial passions, but this is not the case with minerals.

From an early date, Australia has been conscious that Antarctica, even though it is almost entirely icebound, might possess a mineral wealth that would eventually prove retrievable. The Australians have not forgotten the case of Alaska — bought from the Russians by the United States in 1867 for $7 million and widely thought at the time to be a waste of money. Dr Phillip Law, head of the Australian Antarctic office in the 1950s, at that time foresaw for the Antarctic whole mining towns hollowed out of the rock to escape the rigours of the climate and to permit the miners to bring their families. Less futuristically, the Australian ambassador to Treaty negotiations, Keith Brennan, made it clear in 1979 that any oil found off the Australian sector was Australian. [5]

Australia maintains three bases in Antarctica — Mawson, Davis and Casey — and one on subantarctic Macquarie Island. Until recently they have not been noted for their bustle of scientific activity, but the Australian effort has been beefed up considerably, with annual spending increasing from $A8 million (1978-79) to $A18 million (1980-81). Their Antarctic Division has been relocated at Hobart and re-formed as a division of the Department of Science and the Environment.

The legal basis on which the Ross Dependency came into New Zealand's hands is rather a flimsy one, and New Zealand was notably slow in taking up the reins with the Dependency; it was completely ignored by successive governments for the next 30 years. It was the British who protested to the Americans on New Zealand's behalf at the time of Byrd's second expedition. The British Ambassador to Washington complained that Byrd's establishment of a post office and the operation of aircraft and a radio station in the Dependency were undertaken without the permission of the New Zealand authorities.

New Zealand governments have a long tradition of staving off the oft-repeated calls for a greater commitment to Antarctic research. In the late 1950s the Government parted with the finance for Scott Base only under the combined pressure of the IGY organisers and the British, who requested a support base there for Fuch's Transantarctic Expedition of 1957-58.

Of all the claimant states, though, New Zealand has in the past been the most flexible in its position. As already noted, Walter Nash suggested the internationalisation of Antarctica at the United Nations in 1958. During the third Labour Government of 1972-75, New Zealand was known for its internationalist stance, and at the 1975 Treaty meeting it proposed that Antarctica be made a world park.

With the subsequent election of the conservative National Government in 1975, this territorial liberalism was abandoned. An increasing awareness of overseas interest in Antarctica's mineral potential produced a much more self-interested polar policy, and it became apparent that the new government took New Zealand's own potential stake there much more seriously.

To this end, the Minister of Foreign Affairs, Brian Talboys, announced in 1978: "It is often asserted that the Treaty extinguished the claims, or that they were frozen or rendered ineffective. Those who assert that have not read the Treaty. The Treaty specifically provides that the claims shall not be diminished. In practice the Treaty places four limitations upon the claimant state in the exercise of its sovereignty in its claimed territory ... Apart from these four obligations, which constitute the political framework within which scientific co-operation can take

New Zealand's base by Lake Vanda, dwarfed by the dry valley slopes. The base is usually occupied only in summer. A wind sock marks a helicopter pad on the right. *Tony Shaw*

place, the sovereign claims continue as before."

The New Zealand Antarctic programme has operated continuously since 1958, but on a limited budget of less than $NZ1 million a year (1981). Scott Base, on Ross Island in McMurdo Sound, has been rebuilt in an effort to relieve the pressure on accommodation at the old base, which was not designed to deal with the 80 or so people who have worked from it at seasonal peaks. There is also a small seasonal base at Lake Vanda, which has occasionally been occupied during the winter. As part of New Zealand's official presence in the Antarctic, the leader of Scott Base for each year is appointed a Justice of the Peace for the Ross Dependency.

New Zealand's Antarctic programme is run by the Antarctic Division of the Department of Scientific and Industrial Research (DSIR), and is largely dependent on American air support for staff transfer and priority cargoes. Joint logistics are facilitated by the close proximity of McMurdo Station to Scott Base — they are only three kilometres apart. In exchange for this support, the United States uses air and naval facilities at Christchurch, and is exempted from taxation, customs duties and radio station licences. American servicemen stationed at Christchurch — there are up to 700 of them at the height of the

season — are outside the jurisdiction of the New Zealand justice system, but to their credit the servicemen have an exemplary record in the city.

In the subantarctic region, New Zealand has a weather station on Campbell Island, 2,700 kilometres from McMurdo Sound. The claim to Campbell Island has never been contested — it is the southernmost integral part of New Zealand.

The South Americans, who have insisted that effective occupation is the proper criterion for deciding contested claims, have made strenuous efforts to establish their presence in the area of the Antarctic Peninsula. Both Chile and Argentina declared 370-kilometre maritime zones off "their" territories before the Antarctic Treaty came into force. At one time they presented a united front in opposing the British claim, but this has been eroded by Argentina's extension of the western boundary of its claim, and by its refusal to accept an International Court ruling regarding the disputed islands in the Beagle Channel at the tip of Tierra del Fuego.

Various writers have suggested unkindly that the patriotic clamour that accompanies the territorial assertions of the South Americans is designed to distract their respective publics from more immediate political concerns. But there was considerable public opposition within Chile and Argentina to the ratification of the 1959 Treaty — it was viewed as giving away "inalienable rights", and heated debate ensued before the governments ratified it.

The Argentinians have been particularly vociferous in their claim for "Antartida Argentina". They have gone to unusual lengths to reinforce their claim that "Antarctica has taken root and established an awareness in the soul of the Argentine nation" (a quote from the chairman of the Argentine delegation at the 1959 Antarctic Treaty Conference). Argentina now has eight year-round bases in Antarctica — more than any other country — and in the waters around the peninsula the Argentine Navy broadcasts "Welcome to Argentine Antarctica" at the approach of visitors. In 1973 the Cabinet of the Argentine Government held a four-hour-long session on the ice of Seymour Island off the Antarctic Peninsula. When the Chilean president paid a visit to the Peninsula four years later, *La Nacion* of Buenos Aires accused Chile of "territorial claim-staking".

The Argentine Government also decided to colonise Hope Bay (at the tip of the peninsula) "to determine whether Antarctica is suitable for family life", and to reinforce its territorial claims. The first birth in Antarctica took place at Hope Bay in January 1978. Little Emilio de Palma was welcomed by President Jorge Videla as a reaffirmation of "the inalienable role of Argentinians in those far-off lands".

In March 1978 the settlement comprised 18 men, eight women and 19 children — this included five soldiers, their wives and children and two teachers sent to set up a school. The families spend a year at the base; the next summer other families arrive to replace them. Commenting on the first birth in Antarctica, the *New York Times* reported: "Silvia Morello de Palma, the mother of the child, says she hopes her infant son will return to Antarctica. 'By the year 2000 there will be better ways of

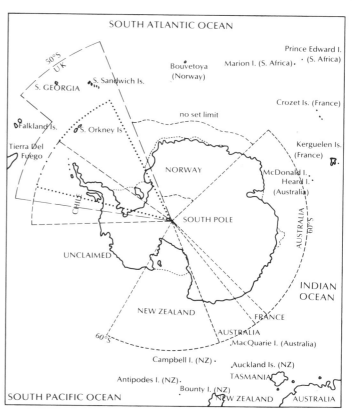

Territorial claims in the Antarctic region. Though shelved by Treaty agreement, the issue of claims has not yet been resolved — and probably never can be, given, for example, the conflicting claims in the peninsula area.

making life comfortable here'." [6]

Chile also maintains its Antarctic activities at a high level, and reinforces its claim with the issue of postage stamps of Antarctica with the Chilean sector marked out. In 1948, the Chilean president became the first head of state to visit Antarctica. The current president, General Pinochet, has also visited Antarctica, in January 1977, the year in which the Chileans established their fourth base there.

The British have three permanent bases on the continent and one in the South Orkney Islands. Since 1962 their territorial claims have been divided up as British Antarctic Territory (south of 60°S) and the Falkland Island Dependencies (South Georgia and the South Sandwich Islands).

France has one permanent base, Dumont D'Urville, on the Adelie coast, as

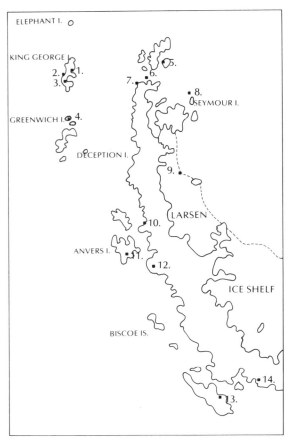

Stations in Antarctic Peninsula area.

1.	Arctowski	Poland
2.	Bellingshausen	Soviet Union
3.	Presidente Frei	Chile
4.	Arturo Prat	Chile
5.	Petrel	Argentina
6.	Esperanza	Argentina
7.	General Bernardo O'Higgins	Chile
8.	Vicecomodoro Marambio	Argentina
9.	Teniente Matienzo	Argentina
10.	Almirante Brown	Argentina
11.	Palmer	United States
12.	Faraday	United Kingdom
13.	Rothera	United Kingdom
14.	General San Martin	Argentina

1960, but made an independent ship-based expedition in 1975-76 and established two temporary camps. Norwegian scientists continue to participate in the scientific programmes of other Treaty nations. In international negotiations, the Norwegians have always had a liberal approach to their territorial claim.

While all the Antarctic bases of the claimant states lie solely within the sectors which those countries claim, those of the non-claimants are dotted all over the continent and the peninsula.

The United States' Antarctic interests have been confined mainly to the west of the Transantarctic Mountains. The American polar programme is an extensive one, co-ordinated by the National Science Foundation which has an Antarctic office in Christchurch, New Zealand. The Americans have four bases in Antarctica, including the Amundsen-Scott Station at the South Pole itself.

McMurdo, the main United States base, is the largest multi-purpose research and logistics centre in Antarctica. The station has its own theatre, chapel and radio station, plus elaborately equipped biological and geophysical laboratories. In summer the population peaks at around 700, with a large shipboard naval contingent as well. Most are support staff engaged in the operation of the two airfields or involved in communications and weather forecasting or maintenance and supply work. Private contractors run the support services at McMurdo.

The Soviet Union has concentrated its Antarctic activities in East Antarctica. Its main station, Molodezhnaya, is the second largest base on the continent. In 1980, after several unsuccessful attempts, the Russians finally established their seventh permanent base, Russkaya, at Cape Burks on the Marie Byrd coast. There is also an important summer base, Druzhnaya, on the Filchner Ice Shelf in the Weddell Sea region, from which a large number of scientists fan out on reconnaissance each season.

well as three bases on its subantarctic islands in the Indian Ocean. These were serviced from Madagascar until that country's independence, but are now supplied directly from France.

Norway closed its Antarctic station in

McMurdo, the largest base in Antarctica, viewed from the air. The road which runs into the distance on the left continues to Scott Base, three kilometres away. On the right, the road leads to Winter Quarters Bay and the dock. Behind McMurdo is Observation Hill, a 240-metre cinder cone, with White Island, also of volcanic origin, in the background. *Official US Navy photograph*

In effect, Russian bases now encircle the Antarctic continent, but their operations there have been unkindly described as "mickey mouse". Visitors to their inland Vostok station, for instance, invariably comment on the crude facilities. The Russians have in the past relied solely on ships for supplies and staff relays, and the high wintering populations at their bases — totalling 260 or more — have reflected this. However, in 1980 a new compressed-snow runway suitable for heavy-wheeled aircraft was completed at Molodezhnaya. The newly opened air route takes more than 24 hours to cover the distance between Antarctica and the Soviet Union, but this compares with up to six weeks by ship.

Japan renounced all proprietary interest in Antarctica in the Peace Treaty of 1951, but it has two bases there — Syowa, on the coast south of the Indian Ocean, and Mizuho on the polar plateau inland from Syowa.

South Africa has one base, SANAE, in Queen Maud Land. It originally inherited the Norwegian base in the same area in 1960, but both that and a subsequent base, SANAE II, became too deeply buried under snow and ice for safe living. SANAE III was completed in 1979. The South Africans also have one subantarctic island base on Marion Island.

Poland and West Germany have revived their Antarctic interests since the mid-1970s and both have embarked on ambitious scientific programmes, largely for exploitative purposes. Neither has made, nor as a Treaty signatory is likely to make, any territorial claims. The Poles are mainly interested in krill, the small Southern Ocean crustacean, and have occupied their Arctowski Station in the South Shetlands since February 1977.

The West Germans set aside $NZ155 million in 1979 for their four-year Antarctic programme. They opened the Alfred Wegener Polar Research Institute at Bremerhaven in February 1980, and have commissioned a special ice-strengthened research vessel of 1,400 tonnes. Their new George von Neumeyer Station on the Ekstrom Ice Shelf on the Princess Martha coast, west of SANAE III, has been designed for 30 scientists. The West German polar programme for the 1980-81 and 1981-82 seasons comprised six separate expeditions with five ships.

They are at least frank about their motives. The English language *German*

35

The construction of SANAE III, the South African base which was completed in 1979. It was designed to replace nearby SANAE II which had become too deeply buried in snow to be safely inhabited. *South African Consulate*

Tribune reported in 1979: "Bonn would like to become a full member [of the Treaty] as soon as possible. In order to qualify it has to embark on comprehensive Antarctic research of its own. Member countries are shortly to allocate exploitation rights in the region and outsiders need not expect to get a look-in . . . Volker Hauff [Technology and Research Minister] is soft-pedalling the Antarctic as a potential source of raw materials. Bonn, as a latecomer, wants to avoid creating the impression of merely having joined to make a quick killing." [7]

The only major world power which is not a member of the Antarctic Treaty is China, a significant absentee, particularly in view of the heavy representation of Warsaw Pact countries. The Chinese have recently established an Antarctic research centre in Peking and are constructing an icebreaker; the first Chinese representatives — an oceanographer and a geomorphologist — to visit Antarctica made a six-week tour, by invitation, of the Australian Antarctic Territory early in 1980. This activity reflects part of the new outward-looking posture of the Chinese, and their interest in participating in international science. It also suggests a likely involvement in Antarctic affairs by China over the next decade.

NOTES

1. *New Zealand Herald*, 15 Oct 80.
2. Quoted in E.W. Christie, *The Antarctic Problem*, 1951, p.254.
3. See, for instance, *The Poles*, Time/Life, 1966, p.171.
4. Grenfell Price, *The Winning of Australian Antarctica*, 1962, p.173.
5. Reported in *Environment* (US), Jan-Feb 1980, p.13.
6. *New York Times*, 23 Jan 78.
7. *German Tribune*, March 1979.

Chapter 4

THE VALUE OF ANTARCTIC SCIENCE

As a remote platform at the bottom of the world, Antarctica has been of intense interest to scientists in a great number of fields, including glaciology, geography, geology, volcanology and meteorology. There is something for almost everyone — even political scientists — and to the concerned conservationist the annual harvest of scientific data is Antarctica's happiest export, providing the least potential harm to the fragile Antarctic ecosystem.

The remarkable natural purity of the Antarctic environment makes it a unique scientific laboratory. Remote from civilisation, it is free from local industrial and urban pollution (though even here heavy metal and pesticide residues from afar have been discovered), and is an ideal place from which to monitor critical world environmental variables. Scientists there have established important baselines from which to measure future changes in the planet's biosphere. But the scientific value of Antarctica hinges on its presently undisturbed state.

The rise of carbon dioxide, lead and pesticide levels in Antarctica reflects the planetary scale of pollution, and is a problem that will become even more serious over the next 20 years. Lead, a toxic metal linked with industrial activity, can-

not be detected in Antarctic snows deposited before 1940. The fact that the lead content of recent Antarctic ice is only 10 per cent that of Greenland sheet ice illustrates Antarctica's distance from the industrial centres of the Northern Hemisphere. Organochloride pesticide residues, including DDT, have been found in penguins at McMurdo Sound, and in krill, penguins, seals and even in snow in the South Orkney Islands.

The changing levels of man-made radioactivity can also be measured in Antarctica, although some local bias in the McMurdo area, where a nuclear reactor operated in the 1960s, is inevitable. Global levels have declined since the 1950s and '60s, following the end of the atmospheric testing of nuclear weapons, but they still considerably exceed pre-war levels.

Antarctica itself has an important effect on the global climate. Recently scientists have come up with the startling possibility that the world's weather over comparatively short periods – 10 to 100 years — may in some ways be influenced by changes in the Antarctic region. World climate is extremely complex. Key factors in its creation are fluctuations in the energy received from the sun, the amount of energy reflected back from the planet and changes in the interactions of wind

Oceanographers sample the waters below the sea ice in McMurdo Sound. Isotopic analysis has shown that even water under the ice shelves is only six years removed from the tropics. But it is doubtful whether the rubbish strewn on the Sound sea floor could ever be removed. New Zealand scientists have been studying both live and fossilised specimens of a microscopic snail-like marine creature called foraminifera whose populations are believed to be particularly affected by pollution and are therefore good indicators of ecological change. *Ray Goldring*

streams and ocean currents.

The Antarctic plays a major role in governing the world's weather because it is the hub of atmospheric circulation and marine currents — and not only for the Southern Hemisphere. Cold Antarctic deep-ocean water is known to penetrate as far as the North Atlantic, and oceanographic studies are steadily shedding more light on how the currents of the Southern Ocean influence the world's marine circulation and, indirectly, world climate.

Scientists have come to see the global ocean/atmosphere system as a giant thermodynamic engine. Heat from the ocean surface — where solar energy is absorbed and stored — is the major fuel for atmospheric motion. In turn, wind currents largely drive the oceans. Through these forces is established the basic motion of the global system: a circulatory heat flow which moves from the tropics to the poles and back again. Even in midsummer the Antarctic atmosphere serves as a global heat sink, drawing warm air from other continents and thus keeping them cooler than they otherwise would be.

In the generation of the global climate, the ice sheet and the vast expanse of pack ice thus play a critical part. Through its relation to planetary heat absorption and sea-level changes, the immense volume of Antarctic ice has more than just a local effect on the Southern Hemisphere. The entire planet is affected by the solar reflectivity — known as the albedo — of Antarctica's ice. Of the solar energy falling on Antarctica far more is lost than absorbed, because the sun's heat is radiated back out into space by the ice sheet. This reflection of solar heat is facilitated both by the very low humidity and the thinness of the air over the polar plateau. Cold air is able to absorb only a fraction of the moisture that warmer air can retain; the extreme cold and dryness of the Antarctic work with the albedo to produce a net heat loss.

The seasonal expansion of the sea ice over the Southern Ocean also has a fundamental influence on the world weather machine. Ice cover drastically reduces heat exchange in either direction between the atmosphere and the oceans. Furthermore, the albedo of ice is four or five times that of water, and even the most minute changes of albedo over large areas bring about new climates, thus amplifying the effects of solar cooling or warming. In winter the Antarctic pack ice covers five times as much of the Southern Ocean as it does in summer. At its maximum, in early spring, the sea ice extends over eight per cent of the area of the Southern Hemisphere.

Thus, fractional changes in the heat output of the sun are magnified in the

Carcasses in the dry valleys. *Above:* A mummified seal in the Wright Valley, some 50 kilometres inland and about 300 years old. Seal and penguin carcasses are found in many places in the dry valleys, without any proven explanation. *Tony Shaw*

Below: The remains of an old Sikorsky helicopter, now stripped of all usable parts. The helicopter tipped over while warming up for take-off, but no one was injured. "It is a handy shelter for lunch while walking from the Lower Wright Glacier to Vanda Station," remarks the photographer. *Tony Shaw*

Antarctic birdlife. *Above:* A brown skua looks over a prospective meal. The natural predation patterns of skuas have been changed by the ready availability of garbage from the bases. *Ray Goldring*
Below: Adelie penguins, the most common of the Antarctic penguins. When constant sightseeing in the 1960s was found to upset breeding, many penguin colonies near bases became specially protected areas. *Ray Goldring*

global climate by the variation of sea ice cover. Scientists have estimated that a mere one per cent decrease in solar radiation would cause an advance of about 1,100 kilometres in the sea ice. This would result in a planetary cooling of 5°C, with catastrophic implications. A decrease of only 1.6 per cent would probably be enough to lead to the world's oceans being completely covered by ice. [1]

This may be an unlikely scenario, but Antarctic science is certainly contributing to a better understanding of the complicated interaction between sun, planet and ice, and to an assessment of how human activity might also be setting ponderous changes in motion.

In the present scientific controversy over the ramifications of the global rise in carbon dioxide, scientific research in Antarctica has an immediate application. Its appraisal of how the "hothouse" effect, amplified at the poles, will bring about the collapse of the West Antarctic Ice Sheet, is so far the clearest benefit that Antarctic science has delivered to the world at large.

Primarily as a result of the burning of fossil fuels (coal and oil), the level of carbon dioxide in the world's atmosphere has risen steadily since the Industrial Revolution, from about 290 parts per million in 1800 to 336 parts per million in 1980. Scientists are now in general agreement that, if present trends continue, carbon dioxide levels will double within 50 years.

Carbon dioxide is important in the climatic process because it inhibits the reflection of infra-red energy from the earth's surface, thus creating a greenhouse effect. Temperature increases of about 2°C have been estimated for temperate zones, but computer simulations have all predicted that surface temperatures around the poles will rise by 8°-10°C as a consequence of the doubling of carbon dioxide levels.

Such a rise in temperature will spell disaster for the vulnerable West Antarctic Ice Sheet. Unlike the East Antarctic Ice Sheet, the base of which is predominantly above sea level, the West Antarctic Ice Sheet is grounded as much as 2,500 metres below sea level and is therefore far more susceptible to climatic warming.

This ice sheet is held in place by the three large ice shelves at either side of it. If local temperatures rise about 5°C above their present level, however, these shelves will quickly disintegrate. This has already been demonstrated, on a smaller scale, along the western coast of the Antarctic Peninsula where, since 1966, about one quarter of the Wordie Ice Shelf has broken away and the other ice shelves have receded. [2] The break-up of the ice shelves would then precipitate the rapid collapse of the ice sheet and generate a rise in the world's sea level of about five metres — not a pleasant thought for the inhabitants of the Netherlands, Florida or Christchurch. A rise in sea level of this degree could well be under way in about 50 years time, and would cause new climatic patterns as well as some inconvenience in coastal cities.

It should be remembered here that we are talking only about the West Antarctic Ice Sheet, and not the entire polar ice cap. The land-hugging East Antarctic Ice Sheet would shrink slowly over thousands of years. Mean temperatures in Antarctica over the period 1958-78 have actually increased by about 0.6°C, consistent with the rise in world carbon dioxide levels during the same 20 years.

In the study of the world's past climate, and its likely future, the ice sheet is a veritable library of our planet's history. To probe its frozen record is to unfold a story of dramatic changes in the global climate over the last 100,000 years. Annual layers of snow are visible in the ice to a depth of 60 metres, and in addition to a register of climate, these layers give an indication of natural levels of particulate fall-out over time. They can illustrate, for example, peaks and troughs in the world's volcanic activity throughout the ages.

At deeper levels in the ice sheet, scientists are able to calculate the air temperatures prevailing in Antarctica as many as

The Garwood Valley in the foothills of the Royal Society Range near the southern end of McMurdo Sound. The large discs of ice are called "kettles" — essentially frozen puddles in the glacial moraine. *Mike Bradstock*

18,000 years ago by analysing the relative abundance of certain oxygen isotopes bound up in the ice crystals. From this they can piece together an accurate record of the last ice age, which was typical of the glaciations that have characterised world climate over the last several million years.

Our knowledge of the ice ages and of how they are triggered off is uncertain. Glaciologists are making a considerable effort to obtain a greater number of deeper ice cores to further these studies.

Astrophysics has also benefited from the examination of the polar ice cores. Scientists have discovered a correlation between high levels of nitrogen in the snow layers and high levels of solar activity, and so can now trace these rhythms back over 400 years. Solar flares and sunspots are thought to have a significant impact on world systems, and some scientists have theorised a link with the onset of ice ages.

Another major area of scientific enquiry in the Antarctic centres on the South Magnetic Pole and its effects on the planetary ionosphere, the envelope of electrically charged particles which encloses the earth and protects life from bombardment by cosmic rays. With the continuous shifting of the earth's magnetic field, the South Magnetic Pole (like the North Magnetic Pole) keeps moving at a rate of about 1.5 kilometres a year, and is now located in the sea somewhere off the Adelie coast.

Many current studies on the upper atmosphere of Antarctica are helping to solve problems on a global scale. Very low-frequency radio waves known as "whistlers" are generated by lightning at opposite points in the Northern Hemisphere and are then received in Antarctica. These radio waves are providing much information on the magnetosphere. Magnetic storms can seriously jam nautical and aeronautical navigation, and the monitoring of magnetospheric changes is therefore important.

The clear, unpolluted atmosphere over the South Pole makes it a favoured location for routine ionospheric observations which have valuable economic benefits in maintaining high quality radio communication around the world. Certain types of cosmic rays, of interest to atmospheric physicists, are channelled towards the poles by the convergence of magnetic lines of force, and thus can only be studied there. Scott Base is staffed all year round to enable the continuous observation of the upper atmosphere.

Meteorites are very useful to scientists investigating the primal evolution of the solar system and the origins of life on earth. Over the last 10 years a large number have been discovered on the ice. One meteorite found by American and Japanese scientists in 1977 weighed 408 kilograms. Amino acids from outer space have also been discovered in certain carbonaceous meteorites. Such acids are the building blocks of life, but these were found to have a slightly different structure from earthly amino acids.

Antarctic meteorites are especially valuable because they have been preserved in more or less sterile conditions, with little oxidation or contamination. Many of those found would have been buried in the ice sheet for tens of thousands of years, and have arrived at the surface only where an edge of the creeping ice sheet has been forced upwards by a mountain barrier.

Even the United States space programme has profited from Antarctica. The primitive soils of the Antarctic were used to develop tests for the Martian soils carried out by the Mariner probes. The German-American space expert, Wernher von Braun, visited the dry valleys in January 1967 to gain some insights into possible environments on other planets. As the story goes, an Antarctic scientist who accompanied von Braun was able to demonstrate to him the crucial role the human eye could play in the detection of alien life: von Braun, with his untrained eye, could not match the Antarctican's ability to find the type of stones that insects like to shelter under. This apparently convinced von Braun of the necessity for manned, rather than robot, missions to the moon.

It is in certain porous Antarctic rocks, too, that intriguing new forms of algal life have been discovered. Known as endolithic organisms, these micro-organisms eke out an existence in cracks and crannies just below the surface of north-facing rocks.

Antarctica's wildlife gives biologists an opportunity to find out how organisms adapt to extreme conditions of cold, wind, desiccation and darkness. Lichens have been subjected to laboratory temperatures of -198°C and survived, while specimens in museum cases have revived, when moistened, after 15 years. Many of Antarctica's tiny insects must "hibernate" for 300 days of the year in order to survive in the frigid microclimates of their sheltered habitats. The biochemical bases of such adaptations may be of more than just "scientific interest". The study of the antifreeze substances in the blood of some Antarctic fish could have practical application — in medicine, for instance.

The ecosystems of Antarctica and the Southern Ocean are remarkably simple ones. But it is this very simplicity which makes them so vulnerable to disruption and depletion. Both the prey/predator relationships within the ecosystems, and the short food chains, are of enormous interest to biologists, for their workings are still not fully understood. Nevertheless, some countries have begun to harvest part of the food chain without careful re-

An expeditioner examines glacial moraines on the lower slopes of Mt Discovery (2,681 metres), about 60 kilometres south-west of Ross Island. Antarctica's ice sheet and glaciers lock up about 70 per cent of the world's fresh water and are of tremendous interest to glaciologists. *Antarctic Division, DSIR*

search into the long-term effects of exploitation. Too much remains unknown about the close interdependence and specialised adaptations of Southern Ocean marine species for such risks to be calculated. With commercial interests developing on the Southern Ocean, marine biology and oceanography have a vital place in Antarctic scientific programmes. We will consider this in more detail later.

Antarctic science is also of tremendous value to geologists in their research into the shaping of the earth's surface. The Antarctic continent is the central piece in the southern supercontinent, called Gondwana, which has fragmented over the last 170 million years and drifted apart to form the southern continents as we now know them.

The theory of Continental Drift, and the cause of the drifting (known as Plate Tectonics), is to geologists what the theory of evolution has been to biologists — a single, unifying framework that provides answers to fundamental questions. Plate tectonics successfully explains such wide-ranging phenomena as earthquakes, volcanoes, mountain-building, past climates and the "youth" of the ocean floors (they are less than 200 million years old). The theory sees the earth's surface as a mosaic of mobile plates, floating like rafts on a more plastic core of hot rock, and in friction with one another as they drift into new positions.

The idea of a giant southern proto-continent was first seriously proposed by an Austrian geologist, Eduard Suess, in 1885. He called it Gondwana after an ancient province of rock in central India. But it was Alfred Wegener who gave the idea seminal form.

Wegener was a meteorologist, a balloonist and a North Polar explorer who was eventually to lose his life in Greenland. In 1915 he published a slender volume entitled *The Origin of Continents and Oceans*. At that time scientific

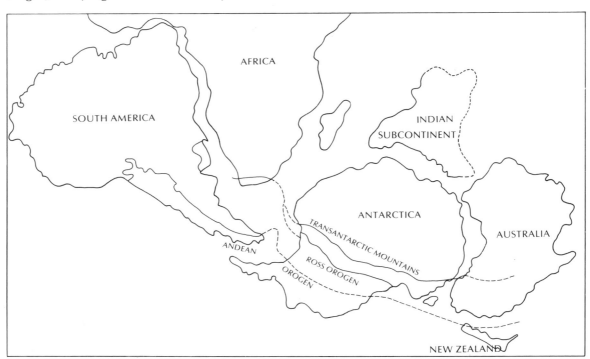

The original fit: the Gondwana continents at the time of their drifting apart, about 180 million years ago. Geological stress lines across the original supercontinent have been traced only in the last 25 years.
Adapted from Wright and Williams/Angela Bodley

knowledge of Antarctica was scanty, but Wegener cited Antarctic data 19 times in support of this theory. Wegener may have consciously modelled his title on Darwin's revolutionary work, for his ideas were similarly ridiculed (for 40 years) before the evidence in their favour grew too strong for rebuttal. Plate Tectonics has assumed scientific respectability only since the 1960s, and indeed is still rejected by the Russian scientific establishment.

Gondwana was made up of the continents of South America, Africa, Australasia, Antarctica and the Indian subcontinent. At various times before its fragmentation the supercontinent was beset with ice. During the Carboniferous period, 350 million years ago, the ancient southern ice cap spread over much of Gondwana, with its centre located over what is now Antarctica.

The study of pollen spores and ice scratches within the glacial sediments in Antarctica indicates that the ice began a retreat by about 280 million years ago and eventually shrank into two separate ice sheets. Later, temperatures became warm enough for the growth of forests on the alluvial plains — even though the Antarctic continent lay within its present polar latitudes. In this epoch, the difference in temperatures between the pole and the equator was not as marked as it is today, and a temperate climate extended from 40°S — about where central New Zealand is today — to the South Pole. The fossil record shows us that unusually large-leafed trees flourished quite close to the pole at this time.

By 220 million years ago, land reptiles and amphibians now long extinct wandered the swamps and plains. *Lystrosaurus*, a small reptile standing about one metre high and about 1.5 metres long, was among them, and with other fossils — first discovered by New Zealand geologist Dr Peter Barrett in 1967 — provided conclusive support for Continental Drift. *Lystrosaurus* was not an animal adapted for long-distance swimming but its remains have been found fossilised in Antarctica, Africa and the Indian subcontinent.

From 190 million years ago there began a major period of volcanic activity which was probably related to the initial break-up of Gondwana. By about 100 million years ago the southern continents had begun to drift apart as new material from deep in the earth's core forced its way to the surface between them and a new ocean floor was created. India drifted north, forcing up the Himalayas as it collided with the northern continent, Laurasia; Australia and New Zealand drifted away and divided about 50 million years ago, while Antarctica drifted back towards its present position.

Fossil trees at Hope Bay on the tip of the Antarctic Peninsula suggest that Antarctica was largely free of ice at this stage, but around 35 million years ago the surrounding ocean began to cool and the beech forests dwindled. The present ice sheet began to form and had covered the continent by 20 million years ago. The growing ice cap had to compete with erupting volcanoes, and in some areas distinctive lava types imply eruptions below thick ice. Although a few million years ago Antarctica had many active volcanoes, only Mt Erebus and Deception Island remain active today. Mt Erebus is one of only three volcanoes in the world with an active lava lake — and the only currently accessible one — and has aroused the keen interest of volcanologists.

Some 20 million years ago, too, Antarctica's isolation from the rest of the world was completed with the formation of Drake Passage. The ice cap continued its gradual expansion, but the polar climate was not yet as harsh as it is today, and New Zealand was sufficiently tropical only 10-15 million years ago to have coconut palms.

About five million years ago, however, the Southern Hemisphere's climate became much more severe and the ice sheet surpassed its current size, expanding

Antarctica as it would eventually look without the ice cap. Studies conducted during the IGY in 1957-58 revealed that the continent actually consists of separate land masses divided by a deep trench which plunges more than 150 metres below sea level. *Lovering and Prescott,* Antarctica... Lasts of Lands, *Melbourne University Press*

to the edge of the continental shelf and rising 300-600 metres higher than its present elevation. Sea ice reached 45°S in the Atlantic and Pacific Oceans over winter, but the circumpolar current kept Drake Passage clear of the pack. Strangely, this ice expansion was not paralleled in the Arctic and for millions of years the world climate was grossly lopsided. The Arctic was an open sea until about 2.5 million years ago and may have been so again even more recently.

In the 1970s the amount of scientific work undertaken in Antarctica remained fairly constant, but there was a significant shift both in the focus and in the methodology of research. General studies are now pretty much complete, and scientists have moved towards investigations of small-scale natural phenomena and the dynamics of the ice, the atmosphere and the Southern Ocean. Their projects have also become much more resource-oriented.

Most Treaty nations have increased their scientific activity over the last few years, but the New Zealand and United States scientific programmes have faced budget restrictions. The United States National Science Foundation budget for its 1980-81 season was restrained at $US55 million — $US4 million less than was asked for. The Americans decided to economise by vacating Siple Base over winter. Several lean years are apparently ahead for the United States Antarctic programme.

Scientific work conducted in Antarctica by New Zealanders is highly regarded overseas, and in per capita terms New Zealand's scientific output is the highest of all the Treaty nations. The emphasis of New Zealand research has been in the earth sciences, with some work on bird life and marine biology.

While scientific productivity is high, the New Zealand Antarctic programme is organised to a tight budget and the scientists themselves condemn the government for its lack of interest and support. Both the New Zealand Geological Society and the Antarctic Committee of the Royal Society make annual representations for a greater Antarctic commitment from the government. They have pointed out that government funding is insufficient to maintain the scientific programme at its present strength.

"The New Zealand Government's expenditure on Antarctic research is grossly inadequate," according to Dr Malcolm Laird, convenor of the New Zealand Geological Society's subcommittee on Antarctic mineral exploration. He notes that New Zealand scientists are extremely concerned over the issue and feels that with such a lack of finance and adequate representation on the relevant international committees, New Zealand runs the risk of having little say in Antarctica's future.

This situation has not gone unnoticed by the nations with Antarctic interests; indeed some American delegates at the 1980 SCAR conference in Queenstown privately expressed to their New Zealand counterparts their concern at New

Zealand's low level of involvement in Antarctic affairs.

But some government ministers and members have recently taken an interest in Antarctic research, although possibly more with an eye to the prospect of exploiting Antarctica's resources than with a concern for pure research. Mr Bill Birch, champion of the "fast-track" development of New Zealand's own industrial resources and Minister of Energy under the National Government, has spoken publicly on Antarctic issues several times and has visited the Ross Dependency. From his comments, he appears to regard Antarctic exploitation as inevitable (see p. 108). His undersecretary, fellow fast-tracker Barry Brill, also made a trip to the ice in 1980.

While New Zealand's Antarctic programme appears to be stagnating for want of support, the Australians are pushing ahead with revamped scientific schedules and support services. In the past the main emphasis of their research has been on biology and glaciology. In 1979 the Australian Government set up an advisory committee, which subsequently reported in favour of a considerable expansion in their research programme. The report stated that Australian Antarctic science was "mainly of high quality but inadequate in size and scope," and pointed to major deficiencies in marine research, the earth sciences, mapping and surveying. Their Antarctic Division has since developed a major new programme in Southern Ocean marine biology.

American Antarctic science has recently become more explicitly mineral-oriented. Scientific teams have been active in their search for uranium and thorium in Victoria Land and in the Ellsworth Mountains. The Russian and West German science programmes have also been heavily angled towards resources. Both countries are investigating krill and other marine stocks as well as minerals. The main objective of the large Russian programme based each summer at Druzhnaya is the evaluation of

Japanese scientists at Scott Base. The Japanese have been particularly interested in the dry valley region and in studies of Mt Erebus. A wealthy Japanese businessman has sponsored successive Japanese investigations in the McMurdo area. *Ray Goldring*

the area's mineral resources. Japanese scientific interest is primarily in upper-atmospheric physics and meteorites.

A major American project of recent years has been the Ross Ice Shelf Project. From a central, summer station 450 kilometres from the open sea on the ice shelf, field parties have carried out ground and aerial studies of the shelf. In December 1977 a flame-jet was used to drill a hole through 420 metres of ice to the water below. An underwater television camera lowered down the 60-centimetre hole discovered — and recorded — life under the shelf. Sampling revealed a sparse population of crustaceans, fish and micro-organisms.

Nearly all Antarctic research is more or less international in that data is freely shared and scientists exchanged. The Ross Ice Shelf Project has had scientific participation from nine Treaty, and three non-Treaty, nations. Many programmes also involve more direct co-operation and joint activity. The BIOMASS project for the Southern Ocean is a prime example; the Dry Valley Drilling Project (1971-76) was a

45

A New Zealand Hercules on the sea ice in McMurdo Sound. Further south, on the ice shelf itself, is the permanent Williams Field, but the sea ice can also be used at the beginning of each season during the major airlifts. The ski-equipped Hercules make a dozen or so flights to the ice each spring, but otherwise the New Zealand Antarctic programme relies on American logistical support. *Ray Goldring*

joint activity between Japan, New Zealand and the United States.

Scientific co-operation is one area in which the Antarctic Treaty has worked very successfully — there is a genuine freedom of scientific investigation anywhere on the continent. Indeed, the scientific co-operation in Antarctic research since IGY is quite unparalleled anywhere else in the world. Sometimes results are published a little laggardly, but the crossing of international boundaries and barriers in Antarctica is a valuable asset in itself. The scientific freedom of Antarctica is much cherished by those working there.

Scientists are understandably anxious that this arrangement should continue undisturbed. Scientific freedom will inevitably be compromised if commercial enterprises are given any place in Antarctic activities. The restrictions on physical access, and the secrecy that is invariably part of commercial exploration and development are completely contrary to the established spirit of scientific co-operation and openness.

Many scientists are concerned that their research efforts should not be distorted by commercial pressures. Prof. George Knox, marine biologist at Christchurch's University of Canterbury and President of SCAR, has commented: "Restraints on Antarctic science programmes caused by rising fuel costs could be a blessing in the long term. Although the restraints would be a blow to some science programmes, the cuts might be a good thing if they slowed the exploitation of krill in An-

tarctic waters." [3] He added that there was concern that pressure from politicians for resource-related research could be to the detriment of basic sciences such as atmospheric and glacial studies, which were still very important.

No one has ever pretended that the quest for scientific knowledge is the sole stimulus for scientific activities in Antarctica. "Strategy and politics rather than science were the major reasons for the increased activity in the Antarctic during the IGY," a polar expert told a Christchurch meeting in 1957. [4] That continues to be the story, with fresh twists, in the 1980s.

As already mentioned, some members of the Antarctic club do very little research there while others who are engaged in Antarctic scientific programmes are not noted for their contributions elsewhere in marine or geological sciences. The Australians are quite candid about their motives: science in Australian Antarctic Territory (AAT) is first and foremost a pretext for an Australian presence. The Report of the Policy Advisory Committee for Antarctic Research, already referred to, sums it up in this way: "The maintenance of Australia's sovereignty over the AAT and its standing in the Antarctic Treaty will be influenced by the extent of scientific and exploration work in which it engages, and by the scope and quality of its contribution to scientific knowledge concerning Antarctica." [5]

While a good many scientists are forthright in their private concern for what is to happen in Antarctica, some have

Above: Pack ice and a captive iceberg in McMurdo Sound. The ice is seasonal and two to three metres thick; the iceberg is small by Antarctic standards. In 1977 satellite photographs of the Southern Ocean revealed an iceberg the size of Australian Capital Territory. *Ray Goldring*
Below: An Emperor penguin and a seasonal camp on the sea ice. The Emperor is the largest Antarctic penguin and stands up to 1.2 metres high. *Ray Goldring*

Pups. *Above:* A seal pup in the McMurdo area. Apart from a small number taken each year for dog food, Antarctic seals are now protected by special agreement. In the nineteenth century, seal colonies on the subantarctic islands and the Antarctic Peninsula were devastated for their oil and fur. *Ray Goldring*
Below: Husky pups, no longer the mainstay of polar transportation but retained for short trips and for recreation at Scott Base. *Chris Horne*

An Antarctic convoy, towed by a bulldozer, crosses the sea ice. Helicopters are used for journeys of any length; field parties generally use snowmobiles. An estimated 19 million litres of fuel are used in the Antarctic each year, mainly for heating and transport. A special blend of diesel, suited to polar conditions, is the predominant fuel. But scientists trying to assess the global contaminants in Antarctic snow and ice must be more and more careful that their analyses are unbiased by contamination from local sources as the engine exhausts from repeated overflights or undue surface traffic taint snow to a surprising degree.
Ray Goldring

denied any sense of obligation and responsibility for their findings. Dr Gisela Dreschhoff, a member of an American mineral reconnaissance survey, in 1977 remarked on the consequences of a large find of uranium: "We are simply scientists. That is not for us to decide. We would simply report the find and then it becomes a political matter." [6] Dr Dreschhoff was in good company — the leader of her expedition was Dr Edward J. Zeller, who has several times proposed that the Antarctic ice cap be used as a dump for nuclear wastes. [7]

Cynics would say that in some ways Antarctic scientists, as individuals, have been fooled into thinking that their research and expeditions could be without political or economic purposes, or that their findings could be an end in themselves. Fortunately, New Zealand scientists by and large are more conservation-oriented and willing to take a stand.

If Antarctic science is to monitor the global changes triggered off by our industrial way of life and to continue to further our understanding of complex hemispheric and planetary dynamics, then it must do so without its integrity being jeopardised by economic pressures or by the environmental disasters that will doubtlessly accompany mineral exploitation.

NOTES

1. J.O. Fletcher, "Polar Ice and the Global Climate Machine", in *Bulletin of the Atomic Scientist*, 1970, 26:10, pp.40-47.
2. J.H. Mercer, "West Antarctic Ice Sheet and CO_2 Greenhouse Effect: A Threat of Disaster", in *Nature*, Vol. 271, 26 Jan 78.
3. *Press*, 4 Oct 80.
4. *Press*, 18 May 57.
5. Antarctic Research Policy Advisory Committee (Australia), "Initial Report to Government", Nov 1979, p.5.
6. *Press*, 3 Feb 77.
7. See chapter 5.

Chapter 5

THE HUMAN PRESENCE

Antarctica has never had an indigenous human population. By the time the human race was spreading throughout the temperate continents, Antarctica was too remote and too frigid to support primitive human groups. If we discount the chance of future revelations from Erich von Daniken, it appears Antarctica's closest human neighbours were the hardy Yahgan Indians who subsisted on the shellfish, seals and otters of the Tierra del Fuego coasts, 950 kilometres from the Antarctic Peninsula. Their comfortless way of life was observed by Darwin during the *Beagle* voyage of 1832-35, and he was amazed at the simplicity of their culture: "They possess nothing; not even beliefs."

With the coming of its first human visitors in the 1820s, the Antarctic wilderness suffered immediate disruption: along the coasts and islands the seal colonies were soon silent and deserted. The presence of men was recorded in other ways too. A naturalist aboard Nathaniel Palmer's later voyages of 1829-31 was to write: "... on their lonely shores the voice of man is seldom heard; the only indication of his ever having trod the soil is the solitary grave of some poor seaman near the beach, and the only wood that anywhere meets the eye, are the staves that mark its dimensions."[1]

Antarctic shores were scarcely touched by men until Borchgrevink's wintering expedition at Cape Adare during 1899-1900. The solid Nordic huts constructed by Borchgrevink's party still stand today, and will eventually be restored as Scott's and Shackleton's huts have been. But that first wintering on the continent left a further human imprint: the grave of the expedition's zoologist, Nicolai Hansen, who died (probably of scurvy), in October 1899.

In the twentieth century Antarctica has been dedicated to science, yet the "pure science" conducted on this pristine continent has carved its name deeply into the few areas of rock unsmothered by the polar ice. Antarctic science has been pure in intent, but graceless in effect. The visitor travelling to the stations in the Antarctic interior experiences an ironical combination of sights. En route the natural scenery is of breathtaking beauty and unparalleled sanctity, but on arrival one encounters a scene disfigured by the litter of supplies and solid wastes. The silence is broken by the incessant noise of diesel-electric generators and tracked vehicles; the drinking water is tainted with the taste of diesel fuel and the air is tinged with the smell of exhausts from internal combustion engines: strange affronts to the concerns of science — and to human sensibilities.

These human scars on the polar plateau are miniscule, however, considering its empty immensity. The rubbish is soon buried beneath the blowing snow — as are the stations themselves — to become veritable "time capsules" in the ice sheet as it creeps toward the sea.

But along the ice-free coasts such a simple "cover-up" is not possible, and time is frozen in another way. In the extreme cold, the natural processes of decay and decomposition are immensely slow, and in the ice-free areas human debris and detritus remain highly visible. To see the remarkable preservation of the food and newspapers of the first British expeditions is intriguing, but the enduring permanence of the McMurdo dump, for example, is less than inspiring.

The total human population is not large. It averages about 700 over winter and around 4,000 to 5,000 in summer. At first thought, the distribution of 33 year-round bases over an area the size of the United States and Mexico combined would not seem too onerous a human burden for the Antarctic ecosystem. But every year, over 2,000 tonnes of cargo and food and some 20 million litres of fuel are brought in to Antarctica, and only a small portion is ever removed. Everything else remains as buildings, machinery, rubbish, particulate matter and gases.

However, quite apart from the problems of waste disposal, the site requirement for human habitation is precisely that for Antarctic flora and fauna: a sheltered area of ice-free rock. So in the cause of science the 29 coastal stations are directly com-peting with the polar wildlife. The effects of this were graphically illustrated at Hallett Station, a joint New Zealand-United States effort established for the IGY in 1957 in the middle of a penguin colony on the northern Victoria Land coast. The station precincts were fenced to prevent the penguins from returning to their annual nesting sites. Contest of land tenure between men and penguins was thus heavily weighted in favour of the humans, but fortunately there was a tacit recognition of the birds' inalienable rights when the station was closed in the 1960s. The area has since been deemed a sanctuary, free from human interference, by Treaty agreement.

There is considerable disruption of local ecosystems in the construction of bases, with their associated facilities for fuel storage and power generation, for aircraft landing and ship docking. However, little thought has been given to their environmental effects. Even in 1977 the Poles made no assessment of the likely effects of the operation of their new station on King George Island in the South Shetlands, although the base was established perilously close to one of the few known three-species penguin rookeries and to a large population of crab-eater seals. Neither was the effect of increased tourism that was likely to result from visits to the station taken into account.

Damage to the local ecosystems by the

A Jamesway hut used by an American construction battalion for living quarters at New Byrd Station in 1962. The hut was assembled the previous year above the snow, but one year later was practically entombed. *Official US Navy photograph*

Snow-melt at McMurdo. As a result of human occupancy, seasonal snow cover of this corner of Ross Island is much less than it was in Scott's time (his original hut is cordoned off on the right). The local snow is discoloured by dust and smoke fallout, thus absorbing more solar heat and melting more quickly. Over summer McMurdo has been characterised as "a dusty western Wyoming mining town". *Ian Campbell*

construction of stations can be seen on the largest scale at McMurdo. As the major logistics centre for the American Antarctic programme, McMurdo has the appearance of a small town. While graced by a cosmetic blanket of snow over winter, by high summer McMurdo is bare and dusty, and has been compared to "a western Wyoming mining town".

To be fair, the station is reasonably well contained, but the slow-growing vegetation in the vicinity has been much affected. Lichens that once occurred within walking distance of McMurdo have completely disappeared, having for too long been sampled by scientists and souvenired by other staff. The hills around McMurdo have been scraped of shingle for roadmaking and are no longer snow-bound in summer. In the 1950s and '60s, frequent helicopter visits by scientists and sightseers to the nearby penguin colony at Cape Royds led to reduced breeding success among the birds, and the colony is now out of bounds by Treaty agreement. The study of the predatory patterns of skuas among the bird colonies of the Victoria Land coast have been impaired by their foraging at the McMurdo dump. Banded skuas from the Victoria Land coast, some 70 kilometres away, have been seen scavenging there.

New Zealanders from Scott Base frequently comment unfavourably on the McMurdo dump, probably unaware that in the past Scott Base had also made its contribution to the extensive rubbish tips by the wharf at Winter Quarters Bay and behind the station. This is not to single out the Americans for special attention: the environmental problems of Antarctic bases are largely ones of scale. The Australian stations have their rubbish dumps too, with some intermingling between buildings and waste: Casey has been described as having "the careless air of a rubbish tip".[2] The Australians have been criticised for their practice of simply dumping their unused food and supplies at the end of each season in readiness for the next year's supplies. The Americans are also reputed to be very wasteful, and "recycling" at the McMurdo tip is an extremely rewarding (though prohibited) pastime for the New Zealanders at Scott Base.

Antarctic bases are now certainly much tidier than they once were. Until the 1970s, polar stations were renowned for their widespread litter, and the disregard of successive expeditions for their immediate surroundings was an unvarying feature of field camps and bases. At the coastal stations, where the ground is continually frozen, the debris associated with the human presence cannot be buried; rubbish and discarded supplies either blow away or remain in middens and dumps, to please only the archeologists of the twenty-fifth century. In the junk heap at Byrd's East Base they will find, for instance, the remains of an Army tank and an artillery tractor abandoned by the Americans in 1941.

Around 1970 an increased consciousness of environmental issues, and the arrival of tourists, resulted in concerted efforts to clean up the bases. A major tidy-up began in the dry valley region, which had been the subject of intensive scientific study, and many old food dumps, unused equipment and the like were removed.

Large rubbish heaps are not the only available means of waste disposal, however, and the coastal waters have been much used for the dumping of rubbish. The only real advantage here is that it solves the problem of visibility, but even this can be mis-managed: the United States Navy dumped 2,000 empty fuel drums into the ocean at Cape Hallett, but many of them washed up on nearby beaches. For many years the Americans left their scrapped vehicles on the sea ice and waited for the summer break-up to take care of them. While many of these

An unusual method of transport — a Rolligon trailer photographed in the early 1960s with fuel drums aboard. The tyres are also full of fuel. With only a few kilometres of road existing on Ross Island, this trailer could trundle only from dock to base to airfield. *Chris Horne*

Rubbish burns on the shore in front of McMurdo Station. The disposal of rubbish and sewage has, until recently, been a conspicuously casual affair at Antarctic stations (a blanket of snow covers a very trashy shoreline in this photograph), and the pall of smoke seen here is just as environmentally offensive as heaps of garbage. As well as contaminating an incredibly clear atmosphere which serves as a baseline for measuring the murk of more populated regions, particulate fallout from the smoke accelerates the melting of local snow. *Ian Campbell*

written-off vehicles now return to the United States by ship, others end up at the McMurdo tip to await the attention of the Scott Salvage Squadron (an ad hoc committee).

Over the last 25 years there has been a dramatic accumulation of inorganic litter at the bottom of McMurdo Sound. Underwater cameras have revealed a great profusion and variety of rubbish: fuel lines, barrels and buckets, rope, clothing, tractors and bits of aircraft. The thousands of beer cans outnumber many of the sponge species on the sea floor. The currents spread the litter over a considerable area, and human debris is commonly seen as far as six kilometres to the north.

While this pollution has probably not damaged the marine life of the sea floor, the rubbish can cover sensitive sponges. "It is reasonable to predict that, in place of the fascinating community there now, eventually the bottom of the Sound will be covered by a veritable rug of litter," comments Dr Bruce Parker, an American scientist concerned about the human impact on Antarctic ecosystems. [3]

Oil slicks and bilge discharge from ships also contribute to marine pollution. Ships routinely pump their bilge tanks while at anchor offshore from stations along the Antarctic Peninsula, and even Jacques Cousteau's *Calypso* was observed to do this in harbour at Deception Island. At the

Two or three years' supply of fuel features in this scene in the dry Wright Valley, outside Vanda Station. Behind the drums stands a meteorological recorder; the sign in the foreground instructs "Do not spit on the footpath". The dry valley region was once strewn with rubbish, left-over supplies and discarded equipment following intensive scientific investigation over two decades, but it has been considerably tidier since the mid-1970s. *Tony Shaw*

peninsula stations garbage is commonly thrown into the sea — to drift onto downwind beaches in a well-preserved state. Frequent oil slicks have been reported from Arthur Harbour (Palmer Station). On several occasions Adelie penguins have been seen emerging from the sea with slicks on their bodies.

In McMurdo Sound, a zoologist with the University of Canterbury, Graham Wilson, has reported oil-coated penguins at Cape Bird, on Ross Island, over 100 kilometres from the nearest base, McMurdo. Over a period of 12 days in January 1979, he noted: "at least twenty Adelie penguins with feathers matted by a dense, black petroleum oil". [4] Penguins are vulnerable to oil because it damages the feather structure that keeps all Antarctic birds waterproof and warm. The birds may also suffer from ingesting the oil while preening. The location of the oil spill at cause was unknown, but fortunately this has proved to be an isolated incident — or at least, an isolated observation.

Antarctic bases have used a variety of methods for sewage and waste disposal. At Byrd's Little America Stations on the Ross Ice Shelf, huge pits were dug in the ice. The story is told that when a frozen pyramid of human wastes had built up, the Americans preferred to level it with a stick of dynamite rather than dig another pit. The effect was apparently close to that described in a profane expression of slang.

Pits are still used at the inland stations, but at McMurdo human waste is flushed directly into the sea, as has Scott Base effluent in the past. At Marambio, on Seymour Island, the Argentinians do up their human wastes in plastic bags: each person seals the bag after using it, then places it on a slide that leads to a nearby dumping ground. Evidently a large number of these bags end up in the sea. If they are sealed properly, the plastic bags will float around for eternity — thus arguing Argentina's territorial claims with a singular effectiveness.

Waste disposal at Scott Base was at first rather haphazard. Garbage was dumped into the tide crack and pressure ridges of the sea ice in front of the base, but spasmodic and unpredictable ice movement in this part of the Sound resulted in a constant regurgitation of waste material. Some of this early waste has been permanently frozen into the rolling ice ridges near Scott Base, but better systems have since evolved, and in the 1980s New Zealand can claim probably the most enlightened approach to disposal problems on the whole continent.

In 1977 a formaldehyde chemical toilet system was installed. This works on a liquid recycling process in order to economise on the flushing medium. When discharged, the sewage effluent is macerated and, along with laundry water and the bulk of chemical solutions from the laboratories, flushed down a heated drain. At the outlet this liquid waste soon freezes into an ice floe, nicknamed the RBT Glacier after the Superintendent of New Zealand's Antarctic Division, Bob Thomson. But even this system has had its problems: some people at Scott Base have found that the formaldehyde fumes cause an inflammation of the genitals.

Field parties and the summer stations at Vanda and Cape Bird use drums and containers for all refuse, including human waste, and these are returned to Scott Base for disposal.

At Scott Base rubbish is either incinerated or, in the case of plastics, rubber products, glass, old batteries, tins and beer cans, containerised for return to New Zealand. In recent years as much as 3,000 kilograms of scrap metal, 600 kilograms of glass and 460 kilograms of plastic have been backloaded each season to Christchurch, where the material is either recycled or dumped on the Waimairi County tip. "Every effort should be made to reduce the amount of plastic products used in packaging," states the 1980 Operations Manual for the New Zealand Antarctic programme, but still not enough attention is given to the types of packaging on stores

The Vanda latrine, with Mt Odin in the background. For economy of operation, urine and excrement are collected in different drums and are then taken to the edge of the sea ice by helicopter. Antarctic temperatures keep sewage odourless. *Tony Shaw*

purchased in New Zealand. There is far more waste material at Scott Base than is strictly necessary.

"Individual awareness both in New Zealand and at Scott Base is still our biggest hurdle," says Colin Monteath, Field Officer for the DSIR's Antarctic Division. Indeed, there is no doubt that conservation in the Antarctic must be promoted as much by the careful selection and briefing of personnel as by the issuing of Treaty agreements. Although science is the official rationale for the human presence in Antarctica, support staff considerably outnumber scientific staff: at the United States bases there is an annual influx of 170 contractors' support workers and 675 Navy people. The level of conservation consciousness among some of these people has been less than desirable, although the

scientific community is not entirely blameless either.

Souvenir hunting in Antarctica is starting to become quite a large-scale operation among helicopter crews, sightseers and even among high-ranking officials. On a helicopter visit in 1976 to a grove of fossil tree stumps on Mt Fleming, east of the dry valley region, the Secretary of the United States Navy, J. William Middendorf III, allegedly removed the central portion of a three-metre fossilised log of great scientific interest. His example evidently encouraged his companions to help themselves as well. "This locality is now well known as a good place for easily acquiring some fossil wood, and is regularly visited by helicopters showing VIPs the local sights," writes Margaret Bradshaw, a geologist at the Canterbury Museum, Christchurch. [5] She reports that helicopter crews have been collecting agate and quartz geodes in large boxloads. Geodes are the attractive result of silica minerals crystallising in the gas pockets in volcanic rock. These are then weathered out by ice and come to rest on the glacial gravel. The American air crews and their "jolly-riders" have been collecting so many geodes that their helicopters have sometimes had difficulty in taking off.

Similarly, the smooth, wind-carved rocks known as ventifacts, which are scattered through the dry valleys, are often picked up by visitors, and on the summit of Mt Erebus American helicopter crews and their tag-alongs "have an unfortunate habit of scooping up (sometimes with shovels) the crystals of Anorthoclase feldspar that are left around the vent after eruption," says Ms Bradshaw. [6]

Scientific parties are generally more restrained in their collecting, but in the early 1970s over 700 kilograms of fossil-bearing rock was quarried from one locality for later study in the United States. Scientists are still waiting for the major study on this collection to be published. Meteorites are also being collected in enormous numbers by Japanese and

American scientists; the Japanese took 400 in one season.

It is difficult to assess how much future scientific research will be compromised by excessive souveniring by both scientists and support personnel, but if present trends continue it seems that certain well-trod areas within range of Scott-McMurdo will soon become denuded of their portable geological assets, to the impoverishment of future studies and aesthetic appreciation.

Some scientific programmes have made their own impacts on Antarctic ecosystems. Entomologists have collected numerous samples of Antarctic mosses and lichens for Berlese Funnel sorting, but this is a wasteful method of screening out mites and other tiny animals from the vegetation, and the constant annual collection of mosses and lichens for funnel sorting has resulted in the disappearance of many local vegetation sites in the McMurdo area. Thus, microbiologists are finding it increasingly difficult to obtain research samples that are free from the effects of previous human presence, and not only in the much-studied dry valley region.

Radioisotopes have been used by scientists in Antarctica for (among other things) the dating of inorganic material. The direct application of isotopes to the water, soil and ice, plus some accidental release, has resulted in radioactivity concentrations far above background levels, and already it has been suggested that Lake Vanda may have enough carbon-14 residues from previous studies to render the accurate carbon dating of its waters impossible. [7]

This has not been the only source of radioactive contamination of the Antarctic, for even this distant continent has not been untouched by the post-war love affair with nuclear energy. Despite the Treaty proviso which bans Antarctic nuclear contamination, [8], the United States operated a nuclear power plant at McMurdo in the 1960s, and a small group of American scientists have made repeated proposals that the ice sheet be used for the storage of nuclear waste.

Nicknamed Nukey Poo, the American nuclear power plant was a portable one developed by the Martin Marietta Corporation and installed by the US Navy in 1962. The choice of site, half way up Observation Hill, a 240-metre cinder cone often climbed by Scott for his astronomical observations, aroused some press criticism at the time: "Ross Island," said

Trucks and snow-cats at McMurdo in the early 1960s "waiting for repair". The Americans are quick to scrap their vehicles: obsolete trucks and equipment are either left on the sea ice just before the summer thaw or are dumped on the McMurdo tip, where they are eagerly scavenged by New Zealanders from Scott Base. *Chris Horne*

A summer view of part of the McMurdo base from offshore. Piles of rubbish can be seen on the shoreline. Half way up the slope of Observation Hill are the buildings which housed the nuclear power plant (nicknamed Nukey Poo), closed in 1972 but not fully decommissioned until 1979. *John Thomson*

the *New Zealand Herald*, "was not much more than a group of volcanoes," with Mt Erebus still quite active. [9]

At the time, however, the Americans were keen to develop nuclear power in remote regions as an alternative to the expense of imported fuel, regardless of Treaty obligations and ecological hazards. The reactor was opened in an expansive flourish of technocratic euphoria: *The Press* glowed that it "would have been impossible without courage, tenacity and selflessness"; [10] Rear-Admiral George J. Dufek wrote in *National Geographic* magazine that the nuclear plant "opens a dramatic new era in man's conquest of the remotest continent". [11] He said that he planned to install four more reactors in Antarctica, this time beneath the ice, but fortunately the poor performance of the military reactors in the Arctic, and of Nukey Poo itself, meant this grandiose vision did not come to pass.

The 10 years of the reactor's operation were an expensive story of shutdowns, fire damage and radiation leakages. In September 1972 a temporary shutdown, caused by coolant water leaking into the steam generator tank, coincided with a Navy review of the economics of the plant. To overhaul the power plant to upgraded standards would have meant the fitting of an emergency core-cooling system. This had not been incorporated in the original design, "since it was concluded that no substantial additional protection of public health and safety would result," but how the US Navy could have avoided a major violation of the Treaty in the event of a loss of coolant accident — and the resulting risk of core melt-down — without such an emergency back-up is hard to say.

The Navy decided to close the power plant down for good, and over the next three Antarctic seasons the installation was demolished at a cost of $US1 million. The reactor was shipped back to the United States and buried, along with 101 large drums of radioactive earth from the site. This rock contained over 200 times the maximum Navy limits on radioactivity. [12] Later, another 11,000 cubic metres of rock were removed at the insistence of the United States Nuclear Regulatory Commission, and this too was shipped through Port Lyttelton at Christchurch. It took a clean-up of six years before the site was declared to be "decontaminated to levels as low as reasonably achievable," [13]and before it was released for unrestricted use. In spite of these levels of radioactivity, workers in the vicinity at the time of the plant's decommissioning were assured that there was no external radioactive leakage.

Neither has the Treaty ban on radioactive pollution of the Antarctic prevented a small group of American scientists from advocating, in the 1970s, that the lethal wastes from the world's nuclear power stations be stored within the polar ice. Such an idea had actually been advanced much earlier by Dr Paul Siple, one of the top men in the United States Antarctic Service. He told a conference of American

An ominous "item" awaiting removal from the nuclear reactor site. Nukey Poo took six seasons to dismantle completely; the reactor vessel, fuel rods and the buildings themselves were shipped to South Carolina and buried at the United States Department of Energy's Savannah River plant. *John Thomson*

industrialists in 1959 that because of the minimal risk to human life, the South Pole was ideally suited to nuclear research and development. The ice cap, he said, "offered excellent facilities for the disposal of radioactive wastes produced by such industries". [14]

While such sentiments may have been par for the course in the heady 1950s, Dr Edward J. Zeller and his associates still envisage the polar ice cap as a global dump for nuclear waste. First put forward in 1973, [15] the proposals amount to an unpleasant combination of linear thinking and hemispheric chauvinism. Virtually all the planet's nuclear reactors are in the Northern Hemisphere, yet with the transport and disposal of their deadly wastes at the South Pole, Southern Hemisphere contamination would inevitably result.

However, Zeller argues, Antarctica has the advantages of international accessibility (the Treaty could be re-negotiated) and an icy remoteness where, safely separated from the biosphere, nuclear wastes would while away the hundreds of thousands of years necessary for their radioactivity to subside.

According to a later revision of the Zeller plan, a disposal area of between 10,000 and 20,000 square kilometres would be required for 25 years' operation, at least 700 kilometres from the coast. The toxic wastes would be contained in metal cannisters. These "hot moles" would be placed on the ice surface and would melt their way to a depth of 1,500 metres over three to five years. Tethering the cannisters would allow them to sink only to a predetermined depth.

But in the light of our limited understanding of the future of the ice cap, and of the tremendous forces at work within it, the safe containment of radioactive material there could scarcely be guaranteed. The logistic support alone for such a project would have considerable environmental effects, with the need for port and airfield construction and staff main-

Crates of radioactive earth at McMurdo prior to shipping to the United States. Chronic radiation leakages from the plant resulted in extensive local contamination, and under the Antarctic Treaty the United States was obliged to remove the contaminated earth from the site. Over 11,000 cubic metres were eventually shipped to Port Hueneme in California via Lyttelton, New Zealand. Although some of this rock contained over 200 times the maximum radioactivity limits set by the Navy, workers at the site were assured that they were not exposed to risk. The reactor site was finally released for "unrestricted use" in May 1979. *John Thomson*

tenance. There are also obvious dangers inherent in transport of the wastes over great distances.

Happily, this ill-conceived idea was rejected outright by the glaciology working group of SCAR, and has never been formally considered by the Treaty nations. That it should be necessary to resort to such extremes for the disposal of the dangerous wastes of nuclear reactors testifies to the tunnel vision and eco-ethical bankruptcy of nuclear power advocates.

The ill wind of the nuclear age might yet threaten the purity of the Antarctic in a further way, if reports of French interest in the Kerguelen Islands as a nuclear testing site prove correct. While the Kerguelen Archipelago is north of the Treaty jurisdiction boundary (60°S), it is still within the Antarctic Convergence, the oceanic and biological boundary of the Antarctic. At the Antarctic Convergence, cold polar water meets, and sinks under, warmer surface water from further north. Both the Treaty boundary and the Antarctic Circle are purely arbitrary limits.

The French Minister of Defence has refused to confirm or deny that there are plans to move the nuclear testing programme from French Polynesia to the Kerguelens, but the islands are known to be under consideration by the French military, who have developed a neutron bomb. Politically and geographically, the Polynesian atolls are an increasingly unfavourable location, while the Kerguelens are, conveniently, without an indigenous human population, are 6,000 kilometres from the nearest human neighbours — and are much less accessible to protest vessels.

In 1980 the French installed microbarographs in the Kerguelens and the nearby Crozet Islands, apparently in order to detect possible nuclear explosions in the Indian Ocean. In addition to endangering the wildlife of the islands, such explosions, with their consequent contamination of Antarctic ecosystems and possible impairment of radiation baseline measurements at the pole, would constitute a blatant disregard for the spirit of the Treaty.

The environmental legacy of the human presence in Antarctica is now being assessed more critically by Treaty governments and their scientists. Over half of the Treaty recommendations so far adopted have been concerned with Antarctic conservation, and the Treaty nations have agreed to prohibit the careless or deliberate introduction of foreign plants and animals to the continent.

The importation of non-indigenous birds including budgerigars and parakeets, which have from time to time been taken down as pets, is also outlawed. The 1947-48 Ronne expedition to the Antarctic Peninsula took poultry, and would have been the first to use alpacas (cousins of the llamas) had not the animals been killed by the dogs in passage.

Huskies have been used in the Antarctic from the outset of human exploration and, with the exception of small laboratory animals imported for experimental purposes, they remain the only mammals permitted there. Scott Base still retains two dog teams for short field trips, recreation and public relations purposes.

Horses and mules were brought to Antarctica by Scott and Shackleton, and left-over bales of their fodder are still in good condition today. Byrd introduced cows, as has been mentioned, but their potential as pack animals was never tested.

Rats and mice have inevitably made

Antarctic huskies, the only introduced animals now permitted on the continent. *Official US Navy photograph*

their way to the Peninsula area but have not, as yet, established themselves at the continental bases. This may be only a matter of time, since stations the size of McMurdo could easily support a cold-adapted strain of rodents. (A mouse got to McMurdo in 1977, but it was probably not the first.) In the past, cats have been kept at bases on occasions, but none have turned feral as has happened on the subantarctic islands.

The introduction of infested birds and mammals could threaten the entomological purity of an ecosystem in which mites and insects constitute the highest forms of terrestrial life. The disruption of the native biology of subantarctic islands by introduced species reminds us that the more favourable Antarctic areas, especially the northern peninsula, must be safeguarded from similar ravages. Across Drake Passage, rabbits were set free as recently as the 1930s and '50s, with predictably dire results for the aboriginal ecology, and reindeer have caused extensive damage to the plant communities of South Georgia.

The flora and fauna of New Zealand's subantarctic islands have also been severely affected by the heedless introduction of animals. Whalers were active on the Auckland Islands from 1849 to 1851, and abortive attempts at farming were made later in the 1850s. With an array of rabbits, mice, rats, dogs, cats, pigs and goats thus found on the various islands of the Auckland group, only on Adams Island have the bright subantarctic flowers once so characteristic of these southern islands survived. Sheep were farmed on Campbell Island from 1895 to 1931, and persist in the wild today, along with cattle, cats and rats. The native tussocks of Campbell Island have been particularly devastated by stock.

New Zealand was, however, the first country to establish reserves for the protection and preservation of subantarctic flora and fauna. The uniqueness of Adams Island was recognised in 1910, and the rest

59

of the Aucklands were set aside in 1934. Campbell Island was not reserved until 1954.

In the Australian sector, the Tasmanian Government proclaimed Macquarie Island a wildlife sanctuary in 1933, mainly through Mawson's efforts. Sheep had been released there in the nineteenth century to supplement the diets of sealers and penguiners, while rabbits, liberated in 1880, caused severe and widespread damage to the native vegetation and brought about erosion on the steep slopes. The sheep have since died off but the rabbits, along with feral cats and rats, have prospered.

Whereas the survival of animals other than rodents in the Antarctic is unlikely, several alien species of plants have appeared at the far northern tip of the peninsula, though these foreign grasses are scattered and sparse. It would, however, be quite possible for the flowering plants of the peninsula to survive in the other coastal fringes which extend beyond the Antarctic Circle. Casey Station would be such a locality, as its environmental characteristics approach those of the peninsula.

Flowers and vegetables have been cultivated in Antarctica. Scott's first expedition grew onions, radishes, turnips and lettuces in boxes placed under the skylights of the ship. A fine powdery soil was dug from Observation Hill, and hyacinths also bloomed aboard the ship. In 1911 one of Scott's men successfully sprouted 12 sea kale seeds in mossy soil at Granite Harbour, on the other side of McMurdo Sound, but colder weather soon killed them off.

During the 1979-80 season, scientists from the University of Waikato conducted a very interesting experiment by cultivating green beans, sugar peas, tomatoes and cornflowers in a solar greenhouse near Lake Fryxell in the dry valleys. The endless day of the Antarctic summer helped to maintain surprisingly high temperatures inside the greenhouse: they averaged over 20°C, with peaks of 35°C. Using solely this natural source of heat, the plants grew and fruited, but only on imported sterile soil.

Scientists and their support staff may have made the greatest human imprint on the white continent, but theirs has not been the only human presence. Tourism by ship and by air has developed slowly since the late 1950s, when the Chilean and Argentinian Governments respectively organised the first tourist expeditions to the Antarctic Peninsula. As early as 1958 Rear-Admiral Dufek, commander of the US Naval Antarctic Support Force, urged New Zealand to open the tourist trade to the continent by sending an inter-island ferry down over the next summer. "The ice to McMurdo Sound is wide open in February, and your inter-island steamer *Maori* could easily get through," Admiral Dufek told a social evening for commercial travellers, [16] but nothing came of his suggestion.

Antarctic tourism began in a serious fashion as the brainchild of travel entrepreneur Lars-Eric Lindblad. His New York travel company chartered the Argentine naval vessel *Lapataina* for a number of cruises to the Antarctic Peninsula, the first of which was in 1965. In 1968 Lindblad Travel ran four cruises — two with the Chilean ship *Navarino* carrying about 100 passengers to the peninsula, and two with the 2,000-tonne Danish vessel *Magga Dan* from New Zealand to the Ross Sea area. The *Magga Dan* became the first tourist casualty when it ran aground at McMurdo in January 1968 and was held fast for several days. Later in 1968 it was proposed that the ship be used as a floating hotel at McMurdo for tourists who would be flown from New Zealand in Air New Zealand DC8s. As the ship could only accommodate 24 people at one time, most of the plane's passengers were to be day trippers, but this idea was stalled for a number of seasons and never eventuated.

Over the last 10 years at least five tour ventures have operated in the peninsula region, but currently only Lindblad Travel

A solar greenhouse and water-heating experiment near Lake Fryxell in the dry Taylor Valley in 1970. Scientists from the University of Waikato grew green beans, tomatoes and cornflowers to the fruiting stage, for with the endless day of the polar summer, temperatures inside the greenhouse averaged over 20°C. Here, Mr Bill Birch, then New Zealand Minister for Science and Technology, talks with Dr Chris Hendy, leader of the Waikato team. *Antarctic Division, DSIR*

and a West German shipping firm are in the business. The Hamburg company runs the 125-passenger *World Discoverer* south from Seattle, while Lindblad Travel have their own ship, *Lindblad Explorer.* Lindblad planned to make six cruises to Antarctica and subantarctica islands in the 1981-82 season. Lindblad prices (from New York) range from $US6,940 to $US12,240 per person for a three- to four-week cruise, some of which have ranged from the peninsula region to McMurdo and then on to New Zealand via the subantarctic islands.

But shipborne tourism has tended to concentrate on the Antarctic Peninsula for several reasons. The peninsula stretches a long way north, and its climate is not quite as harsh as in the rest of Antarctica; ice conditions during the brief summer season are more favourable there for thin-skinned ships. With only a short sea voyage across Drake Passage, the ship-

board tourist is brought to some of the world's most magnificent scenery — a desolate wilderness with an aura of adventure — in only a day and a half. Ushuaia, the southernmost Argentine town at the tip of Tierra del Fuego, is the last port of call on the journey down the east coast of South America, and has undergone something of a tourism boom. A huge modern hotel stands out from the otherwise primitive settlement, and contrasts conspicuously with the Argentine military store.

The peninsula area features a concentration of scientific stations (15 in all), abandoned whaling stations and penguin rookeries. It is well surveyed hydrographically, although despite its navigational aids the *Lindblad Explorer* has run around there twice, in 1972 and 1979, each time requiring expensive rescue and repair operations.

Enthusiasm for airborne tourism in An-

Popular pastimes at Scott Base and Vanda Station. *Above*, a dip in Lake Vanda. A hole has been chipped through the ice, which is here about 10 centimetres thick. Most visitors are apparently persuaded to join the polar bear club and go in at the shore rather than through the ice. Extremities go numb after just a few seconds, in water averaging around 1°C. "No long-term ill-effects, and afterwards you feel great," comments the photographer. *Tony Shaw*

Below, the most southerly and exclusive ski field in the world, some five kilometres from Scott Base, on the slopes at the edge of the Windless Bight. The U.S. authorities forbid their staff from skiing here for safety reasons. This photograph was taken about 3 a.m. *Mike Bradstock*

Wind as a force in shaping the landscape. *Above:* A "wind flower", carved from a pressure ridge of ice. *Ray Goldring*
Below: Sastrugi — wind-sculpted snow. The yellow film carton gives an indication of scale. *Chris Horne*

The human presence. *Above:* This sign, placed by a prankster, is more humorous than the rusting drum on the shores of Lake Vanda. *John Thomson*
Below: Snowdrift melt patterns, formed as a result of dust from human activity, contaminate the snow. Dirty snow warms and melts faster than clean snow. *Ian Campbell*

The *Lindblad Explorer*, moored to the edge of the sea ice at Cape Royds in McMurdo Sound in 1974. The ship's tourists have come out onto the ice to meet a dog team from Scott Base. Antarctic tourism began in a serious fashion in 1965; Lindblad's ships have run aground three times since then, but fortunately without injury. Some have criticised Antarctic tourism as a needless luxury that adds to the environmental stress already sustained by the scientific presence, while others see it as ultimately helping, through education, the cause of Antarctic preservation. *Colin Monteath*

tarctica developed in the late 1960s. The first tourist flight was organised in November 1968 by the Richard E. Byrd Polar Centre of Boston, ostensibly to commemorate Byrd's first flight to the pole in 1929 — although why the thirty-ninth anniversary of this occasion should have merited such attention has not been recorded. Nevertheless, 60 well-heeled Americans paid $US10,000 each for the privilege of flying aboard a specially chartered 124-seat Convair jetliner on a jaunt which encompassed both polar regions as well as all the continents.

A month later, the American airman Max Conrad crashed at the South Pole while flying a specially equipped Piper Aztec across Antarctica from South America to Christchurch. The effort expended in rescuing him was not forgotten by the American authorities, who opposed proposals from Pan American and another suggested joint venture between Air New Zealand and Lindblad Travel. Under this latter proposal, the newly commissioned 2,300-tonne *Lindblad Explorer* would have been based at McMurdo as a floating hotel for tourists flown in from New Zealand. Rear-Admiral D.F. Welch complained in 1970 that "Plans for tourism have given me fits in the past year," [17] and pointed both to the dangers of the hostile polar environment and to the nuisance tourists would create for scientists working in Antarctica. Tourism would detract from the scientific value of Antarctica, he explained, and already scientists were beginning to worry about pollution levels and the effects of human activity on the environment.

63

New Zealand Antarctic authorities were also worried. The Superintendent of the Antarctic Division, Mr Thomson, warned that tour parties would need to be self-sufficient, as facilities for scientists in Antarctica were already under strain, and he noted prophetically that there was little that could be done in the event of an aircraft mishap on the ice.

Common sense thus prevailed and Pan American and Air New Zealand were dissuaded. The hardening attitude to tourism was reflected in the United States Navy's refusal in December 1970 to allow another "Byrd Memorial" flight — this time for the forty-first anniversary — to land at McMurdo. Two months later the harebrained scheme of another American adventurer, to make a snowmobile expedition to the pole in order to salvage Conrad's aircraft, was similarly blocked by the Navy authorities. Mr Walt Pederson's expedition was very poorly prepared, and he was not even sure whether sufficient fuel had been arranged.

The conflict of tourist and scientific interests appeared to have reached a compromise with the overflights which the Australian airline Qantas inaugurated in February 1977. Both Qantas and Air New Zealand made day excursions in wide-bodied jets, carrying 250 to 350 passengers, for several seasons. Fears for their general safety were expressed in many quarters, however. Two months before Air New Zealand's Mt Erebus disaster of November 1979, Treaty members at the Tenth Consultative meeting in Washington had pointed out the dangers involved in overflights in the turbulent Antarctic atmosphere. Unlike the Arctic, with its well-travelled air space, Antarctica lacks the necessary radio beacons, meteorological stations and emergency services, while navigation is made more difficult by sunspots, which sometimes completely black out radio communication.

The tragedy of the 257 lives lost in the Erebus air crash has underlined the hazards of polar aviation and the dangers inherent in inadequate briefings and safety precautions in such adverse conditions. Antarctic bases are not equipped to cope with disasters of such magnitude.

Qantas made its twenty-fifth polar excursion only five days after the DC10 crash, but their Boeing 747 was at least equipped with emergency polar survival suits — including overshoes and a furlined hood — for each of the 300 or so passengers. However, any further Australian overflights will be charters only, and Air New Zealand is plainly unwilling to risk further aircraft or their passengers. Antarctic overflights may continue in the form of transpolar flights between Argentina and New Zealand which were begun by the Argentine national airline in 1981 on an irregular basis. The Chilean national airline, LAN-Chile, has also expressed interest in transpolar flights.

The development of further airborne tourism appears unlikely, for the costs involved in the landing of civilian aircraft on the ice are prohibitive. The requirements for airlines are much stricter than those for military air operations, and the provision of adequate facilities for radar and traffic control, fuel and servicing, as well as tourist amenities, would prove extremely expensive. There has been talk from time to time of hotel building in Antarctica, either at McMurdo or at Marambio, where the Argentinians have frequently been rumoured to be strongly in favour of such a venture. However, the costs of construction, maintenance and staffing could scarcely be offset by the seasonal returns, and there would be serious environmental problems besides.

The Treaty nations have been attentive to the need for the careful regulation and monitoring of tourism in Antarctica. When the first tourist expeditions to McMurdo Sound were organised in 1968, policy statements were formulated by the New Zealand and American Governments to regulate numbers and the frequency of visits. Today Treaty nations try to concentrate tourist landings in special areas where the effect of the visitors can be monitored and assessed before further controls are brought in. Recommendations have been made at the consultative meetings, some of which have dealt with the special measures to be observed by tour organisations. Tourist ventures are to comply with the Statement of Accepted Practices: tourist groups can visit only those stations for which permission has been granted, and land only within specified Areas of Special Tourist Interest. They are also obliged to report on their activities, giving numbers, places visited and dates of landing.

The best level of tourist regulation can come from the Antarctic bases themselves, for they have considerable control over the way in which groups are organised. Antarctic scientists and staff have had mixed reactions to the advent of tourism. Dr Bruce Parker, an American scientist concerned about Antarctic conservation, has announced that "irresponsible tourism remains the greatest threat to the Antarctic Peninsula". [18] Some have criticised the elitism and privilege of Antarctic cruises, while others have pointed to the constructive influence Antarctic tourists have had through their contributions to *Audubon* and other conservationist magazines.

Colin Monteath, of the New Zealand Antarctic Division, is one who considers tourism to be justifiable in the Antarctic. "I have been impressed by the calibre of the *Lindblad Explorer* tourists," he comments. "They are very interested in the protection of Antarctica and are far more concerned than many of the people working in Antarctica today." He emphasises that "everyone in Antarctica is essentially a tourist, and as tourists we have had a major impact on the Antarctic environment. Damage to the environment is often whitewashed and largely ignored because it is under the auspices of Science."

Antarctic tourism did bring about a rapid assessment by the Treaty nations of their own attitudes to conservation.

The wreckage of the Air New Zealand DC10 on the slopes of Mt Erebus. Limited visibility was one of the principal factors behind this 1979 disaster in which 257 lives were lost. Several months earlier a meeting of the Antarctic Treaty nations had warned of the dangers of tourist overflights in the turbulent Antarctic atmosphere; even had the jet succeeded in making a crash landing, there would have been no provision for polar survival on board. *Ray Goldring*

Although many Antarctic bases are still eyesores, most are considerably cleaner and tidier than they were in the 1960s. Tourism also prompted the much needed repair and maintenance of historic huts and monuments. Scott's original hut is in a poor state of preservation, having been the victim of souvenir hunters and graffiti artists. However, the huts at Cape Evans and Cape Royds have been preserved more or less as the expeditions left them, thanks to extensive restoration work by New Zealand Antarctic Society caretakers. The Treaty nations have recognised 43 historic sites worthy of protection and preservation in Antarctica; among these is Mawson's hut at Cape Denison which is now to be restored by the Australians.

With the increasing interest of Japanese and West German tourists in the scenery of the Antarctic, ship-borne tourism is likely to expand over the next decade. Its localised effects must be watched carefully, just as the impact of the scientific presence in Antarctica is also now starting to be properly evaluated. Unless closely regulated, tourist detritus and wildlife disturbance is inevitable: cigarette packets and film wrappers degrade extremely slowly in the sub-zero temperatures of Antarctica. One observer noted the unusual find of half a dozen cases of watermelon floating along with other flotsam in the waters off the peninsula soon after a cruise ship had passed that way. [19]

To be sure, control over tourism can never be absolute, given the unusual legal status of the continent. But while it will be some time before the impact of tourism on Antarctica could be equal to that created by the scientific presence there, the proper surveillance of tourism is of primary importance.

NOTES

1. James Eights, *Voyages to the South Seas . . .*, 1838.
2. *Bulletin*, 18 March 80.
3. Lewis and Smith (eds.), *Frozen Future*, 1973, p.410.
4. *New Zealand Antarctic Record*, Vol.2, No.2, 1979.
5. *New Zealand Geology Society Newsletter*, 1978.
6. ibid.
7. Reported in *Environmental Science and·Technology* (US), June 1980.
8. Antarctic Treaty, Article V (1): "Any nuclear explosions in Antarctica and the disposal there of radioactive waste material shall be prohibited."
9 *New Zealand Herald*, 13 Dec 61.
10. *Press*, 6 March 62.
11. *National Geographic*, May 1962.
12. *US Antarctic Journal*, March 1980.
13. ibid.
14. *Polar Times*, March 1959.
15. See *Bulletin of the Atomic Scientists*, Jan 1973.
16. *Press*, 20 Sept 58.
17. *Press*, 6 Feb 70.
18. Parker (ed.), "Environmental Impact in Antarctica", 1978, p.362.
19. *New Zealand Environment*, Summer 1978.

Chapter 6

CLOSING IN FOR THE KRILL

Journalists struggled for a long time to come to terms with the krill question before they triumphed with the above headline. Diplomats, businessmen and scientists have also struggled, sometimes in close combat, to reach some sort of agreement on fisheries management in the Southern Ocean. Krill have been of primary interest because of their seemingly huge abundance, and although there has not been much of a ready market for them, they were ballyhooed throughout the '70s as a cheap answer to the world's protein shortage.

Krill is a Norwegian term meaning "small fry", and actually refers to many species of planktonic crustaceans. By far the dominant species, *Euphausia superba*, a semi-transparent, shrimp-like creature with an average body length of 50 millimetres and 25-millimetre antennae, also goes by the common name krill. It is this species which is referred to in all discussions of krill's economic potential.

Krill are omnivores which feed on other animal plankton as well as the abundant phytoplankton (mainly diatoms) which bloom in the upwelling of the nutrient-rich polar waters. At night they light up to become a mass of blue-green bioluminescence, and this regular swarming habit makes for their easy harvest. They are found both north and south of 60°S, the political delineation of Antarctica, but stay south of the Antarctic Convergence, where the cold polar water meets warmer

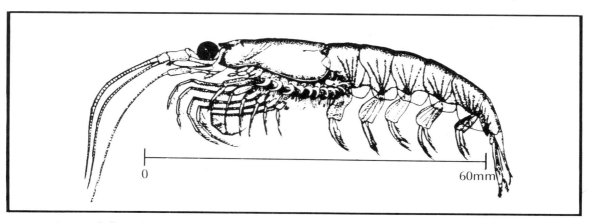

Antarctic krill (*Euphausia superba*). Their huge abundance caused much optimistic speculation in the 1970s that they might be a ready answer to the world protein shortage; their swarming habit also made them easy to net.

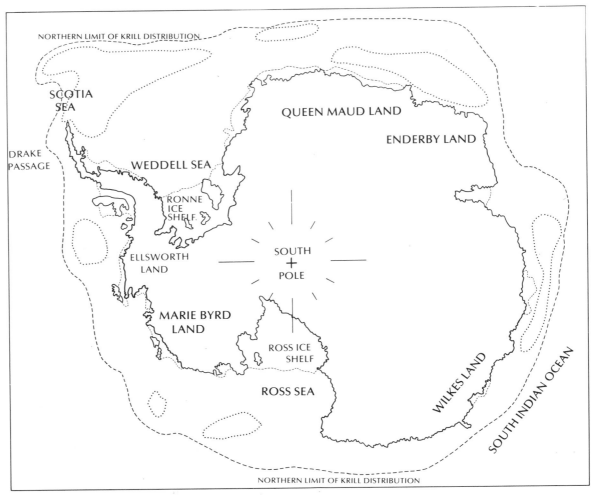

The concentration and distribution of krill in Antarctica. Krill are cold-loving animals and remain south of the Antarctic Convergence, where Antarctic waters meet warmer currents from the north. Their major concentrations are shown within the dotted areas.

water from the north. The Convergence forms a natural barrier for the cold-loving krill.

Krill are found right around the continent, but concentrate themselves in the Atlantic and Indian Ocean sectors and around the Weddell Sea. In winter they are covered by the pack ice, so that whales and fishery vessels can harvest them only in the summer season when the pack ice recedes. However, different age groups of krill swarm separately.

A Russian exploratory venture in 1964

marked the beginning of commercial interest in the krill, whose high protein content has been the main attraction for the fishing nations. In the live state krill can contain as much as 16 per cent protein and seven per cent fats, while in processed form they can rate up to 50 per cent protein. They are also a potentially significant source of A, D and B group vitamins and are unusually rich in calcium, copper, iron, magnesium and phosphorous. Thanks to their remote habitat and their low place in the food chain, however, they contain only very low levels of heavy metals and fallout.

Very high estimates were made in the late 1960s and '70s of both their standing stock mass and their productivity, but these calculations were based on scant data. Estimates from krill standing stock have varied by almost a factor of 10, from about 180 million tonnes to 1,350 million tonnes, and in the light of their relative longevity (three to four years, more than other animal-plankton), there is still some debate on their productivity. It was thought that their abundance stemmed from the depletion of whale stocks and the failure of other species to take up the slack. Some extremely grand projections were thus made of possible krill catches. The United Kingdom Fisheries Research Board suggested that 50 million tonnes could be taken annually on a sustainable basis, while the United Nations Food and Agriculture Organisation (FAO) in 1970 estimated annual catches in the region of 100 million to 150 million tonnes. When one considers that the total world marine catch stood at 73 million tonnes in 1976, one can only gasp at the effect on the Southern Ocean of such a huge fishery — supposing in fact that krill stocks could sustain such harvests.

Although there has been little sign so far that the developing nations will ever benefit from the exploitation of krill, they have been advertised as the answer to the hunger pangs and chronic protein shortage of Third World countries. The FAO and related organisations have since had their excitement dampened, and world hunger has not been a motive in the development of the fishery by the industrial nations which alone possess the capital and sophisticated technology needed to harvest and process this inaccessible, and difficult, crustacean.

It is an expensive business. A 1977 report made to the FAO concluded that krill products will be "generally sophisticated and costly. The cost and earnings cannot yet be predicted with sufficient precision to satisfy administrators, bankers or entrepreneurs ... the utilisation of the resource will tend to be limited initially to a few of the developed countries." [1]

The major fishing nations have found the possibilities of krill attractive not only for the protein stakes. Overfishing and marine pollution have had serious effects on world commercial fish stocks. Despite huge increases in investment in the oceanic fishing fleet since 1970, the world fish catch has levelled off, and the catch per dollar has fallen sharply as traditional fishing areas have been depleted. The catch return per dollar of commercial species such as herring, tuna, cod and sardine has been reduced by 40 per cent in recent years, despite the increased tonnage of fishing fleets and a greater sophistication in their fish-locating equipment and catching gear. The fishing nations have been eager for an untapped marine resource for political reasons as well, and many coastal states have adopted 370-kilometre exclusive economic zones (EEZs — usually known as the 200 mile zone). If 370-kilometre maritime zones were adopted by all nations, the use of the most productive 35 per cent of the world's oceans would be severely limited: the impact of fishing restrictions on the Soviet Union alone is estimated to be an annual catch reduction of six million tonnes. Understandably, the Soviet Union has led the way in experimental krill exploitation, and its economic interests in krill made it an unco-operative negotiator in the draft convention discussions for the Southern Ocean.

The fishing season for krill is short (three to five months) but from January to April swarms, which can be located with echo sounders, may contain a density of between 10 and 16 kilograms of krill per cubic metre. The maximum catch rate achieved by a West German experimental trawling expedition was 30 tonnes in eight minutes, with an overall catch rate of 8-12 tonnes per hour. Even the Russians, who are not reputed to be good fishermen in the Southern Ocean, have in recent seasons consistently exceeded 100 tonnes per day. Annual catch rates for all nations were estimated by the FAO to total around 20,000-40,000 tonnes in the early '70s, although some countries were unwilling to disclose actual figures on what was known to be a sensitive subject. Since then, the total annual catch has risen steadily as fishing has become less experimental and more intensively commercial.

Nevertheless, krill fishing has had a slow start. The great distance of Antarctica from the major fishing nations, and the lack of support services over most of the Southern Ocean, were drawbacks to be overcome. Moreover, krill are caught by mid-water trawling, a technique quite different from conventional bottom trawling and one requiring sophisticated technology; powerful vessels are needed because of the high drag of the small-meshed nets. The trawlers must be equipped with large processing decks, and only a limited tonnage of krill can be landed per day. This is because krill begin to spoil after only a few hours on deck, even in very low temperatures. Their organs, particularly the liver and stomach, contain highly active enzymes which cause rapid breakdown and taint the meat. When intended for human consumption, krill must be processed within four hours, as opposed to 12 hours if the catch is to be turned into krill meal for stockfeed. Krill are hard to preserve, and many methods have been tried. Deterioration continues even in the frozen state unless the krill are frozen rapidly to a temperature below -20°C and then stored at this low temperature.

Despite these difficulties, the Soviet Union and Japan are already undertaking routine commercial harvesting and marketing of krill. Whole krill have had satisfactory sales in Japan, where a small native shrimp is a traditional food item. The flavour and texture is highly variable, however, and the product sometimes develops a sharp, metallic, "cold storage"

flavour and a bitter aftertaste. The Russians have marketed a krill paté ("Okean"), a cheese spread, a shrimp butter, krill snacks and sausages. The cheese spread ("Koral") has been particularly successful, but the production of paté ceased when sales were lower than anticipated — even though consumer response was reported to be good. Both the Japanese and the Russians produce delicatessen krill lines, but these, too, are of a limited sales potential. West Germany is looking towards protein concentrate for animal feed, while Chile produces frozen krill "sticks", which are rather like fishfingers. The Norwegians have also used

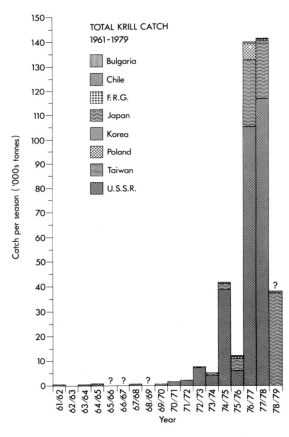

Depletion of other fisheries and increasing foreclosure by 370-kilometre maritime territories forced the major fishing nations to exploit Antarctic krill on an unprecedented scale in the mid-1970s. Technological advances also gave better catches. *Don Robertson*

krill in soup products, with good quality reported, and a Swedish company has produced an edible protein which tastes and smells like crabmeat.

Krill meal as an animal feed has been manufactured on a commercial scale by the Russians and Japanese for some years. It has passed extensive feeding trials with generally good results — although in Polish experiments cows fed on krill meal had a high incidence of abortion. Russian experiments with commercial salmon raised on krill were very successful: the red pigments of the krill give a commercially desirable pink colour to the flesh of the fish. However, the production of krill meal entails higher costs than does meal from other industrial fish species and it is not as profitable as the processing of krill for human consumption.

Within the developing krill industry, the competition is for markets rather than for raw material. Consumer research and test marketing have been essential, for the selection of end-products determines processing requirements and the overall system of exploitation. Although the Russians have been fishing krill commercially since 1970, the world krill industry is still very much in the experimental stage. The true saleability of krill products is unknown, and potential revenues cannot be estimated because marketing trials have fixed their products at fairly arbitrary prices.

If the economics of catching krill still remain to be evaluated, the possible ecological effects have hardly been contemplated by fishery advocates — although conservationists are drawing attention to the dangers involved.

The importance of krill in the Antarctic marine system cannot be over-emphasised. They are the predominant animal-plankton species, and constitute the principal link in the natural economy of the Southern Ocean. Krill provide the major food supply of five species of whale, three species of seal, 20 species of fish, three of squid and numerous bird species, including penguins. This dependence of so many predators on one prey group is extremely unusual.

The short length of the Antarctic marine food chain is also responsible for the fragility of Antarctica's ecosystem. Complex food chains are inherently more stable than simple ones because as the number of feeding inter-relationships increases disruption of any one part becomes less important in the overall balance of the ecosystem. But one can hardly imagine a simpler chain than that which extends from tiny plant plankton to the largest of whales, via krill.

It seems that large numbers of predators can utilise krill because of a finely evolved system for sharing out the resource. Predators feed in different locations, on different age-classes of krill, at different times of the year and at different depths. In addition, the swarming habit of krill allows even very large predators such as the baleen whales to feed on them efficiently. Not only do different species of baleen whales feed on different sizes of krill, but the time of each whale migration is also tuned to the krill life cycle. This specialised feeding pattern is a good example of how marine creatures have resorted to a vast array of evolutionary adaptations in order to thrive in the cold Antarctic waters.

The Southern Ocean whale populations are under great stress. Although fin, blue, humpback and southern right whales are now protected, their present population sizes are only a small fraction of the estimated original stock. It is recognised that baleen whales currently do not take a large share of the krill standing stock but a rapid recovery, or any recovery at all, requires continued access to an abundant food supply.

A complex re-adjustment of the entire Antarctic marine ecosystem was set in motion by the whaling industry. Harvested krill come from the total now consumed by predators and not from some hypothetical part of the stock no longer grazed upon by the depleted whale

Adelie penguins and chicks at Cape Royds, with a relic from the Shackleton expedition. Like many Antarctic bird species, Adelies are dependent on krill as their major food source. The abundance of krill gives them a crucial place in the Southern Ocean food chain. They are also the main food of the baleen whales, 23 species of fish and squid and three species of seal. *John Thomson*

population: there is strong evidence that the slack has been taken up by other species. Female crabeater seals, which feed extensively on krill, are maturing earlier, while there has been a definite surge in the penguin population. Along the Antarctic Peninsula and off-shore islands, where whales were once concentrated, penguins have extended their range and numbers have increased dramatically, with competition for nest sites indicating possible overcrowding in some places.

Accurate information on the standing stocks and sustainable yields of krill are lacking, and there are very significant gaps in our understanding of krill biology and productivity and of how they are preyed upon by other levels in the Southern Ocean food chain. It is known that krill are relatively long-lived, but there is still considerable doubt about total life span and the age at which sexual maturity is reached; their productivity may be com-

paratively low. A sustainable yield cannot be calculated without also knowing the rate at which the krill population is replaced.

Antarctica's apparently large stocks may be tempting to the fishing states, but it should be remembered that in the managing and harvesting of populations the rates of maturity and productivity are more important than the size of stocks at any particular time. The harvesting of the tropical wet forests has been a case in point. Many companies saw huge profits through timber production, but each of their trees took many years to grow.

The biology of the Antarctic has not been studied sufficiently to allow anyone to predict with confidence the effects of tampering with Southern Ocean food chains. Even though krill are very abundant, the entire ecosystem is vulnerable to bad management and over-exploitation of stocks; all indications point to the need to regulate the developing krill fishery very carefully. A parallel with the Peruvian anchoveta industry can easily be drawn here.

Anchoveta are very small fish which feed on phytoplankton off the Peruvian coast. The phytoplankton are nourished by a cold but nutrient-rich ocean current (the Humboldt) flowing northwards from Antarctica. Practically unknown until the 1950s, anchoveta soon constituted one-sixth of the total world fish catch, and a heavy investment was made in processing them into fish meal for export as stock feed. In 1967, the catch was nearly 10 million tonnes, but five years later the fishery had virtually collapsed, mainly from gross overfishing.

Concern was expressed among the Antarctic Treaty nations that the growing interest in krill should be regulated before a full-scale industry got under way, and this has led to a management regime for the entire Southern Ocean. In May 1980, the Treaty nations, together with a number of observers from such organisations as the FAO and the International Whaling Commission (IWC), met in Canberra to approve the final draft of a Convention on the Conservation of Antarctic Marine Living Resources. This convention was opened for signature in August 1980. The need for such protection had been formally noted by the Treaty states in 1975, and subsequent meetings in a number of countries allowed the details of a draft convention to be prepared.

The Convention contains innovative conservation standards that amount to quite a landmark in international law. It is to apply further north than the Treaty limit of 60°S, and its boundaries are to be ecological: it covers all living marine resources south of the Antarctic Convergence. One anomaly in this approach, however, is the exclusion of whales and seals from its coverage, for they are the subject of other conventions.

The Convention also adopts an "ecosystem" approach in which the harvesting of the target species is to be carefully considered in relation to its consequences for other dependent species. A commission established under the convention in Hobart will compile, analyse and publish data on marine populations, on catches and fishing effort, and will adopt conservation measures. These may include regulations on open and closed seasons and areas, on methods of harvesting, and on quantities to be harvested.

Though it appears to be developing an interest in mineral exploitation, New Zealand showed a strong interest in the conservationist approach to marine resources at Canberra. It was at New Zealand's suggestion that the Convention now includes an article (XI) which provides for co-ordination between conservation measures within the area covered by the Convention and those pursued in adjacent marine areas.

Other Antarctic seabirds depend indirectly on krill through their diet of fish and squid. A sooty albatross chick calmly contemplates the photographer on a subantarctic island. *Antarctic Division, DSIR*

But because of the political problems caused by the sovereignty dispute, the Convention does not come to grips with the important questions of national quotas and the enforcement of conservation measures. The Convention is really far more oriented toward fishing than toward protection and conservation. The voting procedures do not favour the establishment of strong, conservationist regulations and there is no provision for a permanent scientific staff to plan research, evaluate data and recommend conservation measures. It is hoped that the Scientific Committee, an advisory body to be set up by the Convention, will be given more power than that associated with the IWC, which has been an unencouraging precedent. Implementation of the "ecosystem-as-a-whole" conservation standard will require from the countries involved a commitment to support a substantial, long-term scientific programme and a willingness to limit krill harvesting until sufficient data is available to make scientifically sound decisions.

A major weakness of the Convention is its failure to create even interim harvest quotas. The United States originally suggested a figure of two million tonnes a year as the aggregate krill catch, but this was dropped at the Canberra meetings. The proposal was blocked by the Soviet Union, with support from Poland and Japan — the nations with the biggest investments in the krill stakes. The American quota proposal also lost the approval of many environmentalists who were concerned that it would encourage some states to expand their fishing operations too rapidly. In its place, a rather weaker United States resolution was accepted; this calls on the parties entitled to become members of the Commission to show "the greatest possible care and concern" in any harvesting of Antarctic marine living resources in the period prior to the Convention's coming into effect.

This may not prove strong enough to protect the food of species such as the blue and humpback whales, which are already critically scarce in the Southern Ocean. A survey of the whale populations in Antarctic waters was made for the IWC by a team of scientists in early 1981. In two months they spotted only 17 humpbacks and a mere seven blue whales. Even a blanket interim limit on krill catches would not necessarily be enough either, for what will most influence the survival of the whales is the preservation of their feeding grounds. Blue whales, for example, tend to feed on the krill swarms near the pack ice, so the creation of fishing zones may be as important as the actual numbers of krill taken.

Total allowable catch limits are particularly important because it may be five or 10 years before the Convention comes into force and the commission establishes binding measures. The Convention for the Conservation of Antarctic Seals — animals not currently exploited — was signed in 1972 but came into force only in 1978 after it had finally been ratified by seven of the 13 signatories. The Agreed Measures on Conservation for Antarctic Flora and Fauna was concluded by the Treaty governments in 1964 but have not yet been ratified because of technical and legal hitches in some countries. Meanwhile, they are accepted as informal guidelines. Given the economic interest in krill and the potential for conflict in effecting the conservation controls, it seems quite possible that the Marine Living Resources regime may never actually be enforced.

The Soviet Union, perhaps the most important of the powers opposing a conservationist convention, gave an indication of hard-line future attitudes when it proposed an amendment which, if accepted, would have scrapped the "ecosystem" concept in favour of a catch system based only on consideration of species directly associated with the harvested species.

The ecosystem approach is vital to krill management because krill are so low in the food chain. Geographic considerations will also be important, as the two areas of greatest abundance of krill — the Scotia and Weddell Sea regions — are the only known areas of krill spawning. Over-exploitation of krill that are about to spawn would jeopardise the maintenance of a breeding stock and thus care must be given to local harvesting effects. Some regions would support high sustained yields, others might not. Krill-swarm disruption could give rise to population crashes in some areas.

Recent research based on the ecosystem approach has produced much lower es-timates of sustainable yields than those much-publicised figures of 100-150 million tonnes annually. In 1978, some American scientists suggested that in order not to hold up the recovery of whales, the interim catch of krill should not exceed 10-25 million tonnes. Soviet scientists have scaled down their estimates too; some are now talking of a 15 million-tonne annual sustainable catch.

These lower figures would still make krill the world's largest fishery — in 1976 only 10 fisheries in the world recorded catches of over one million tonnes, with

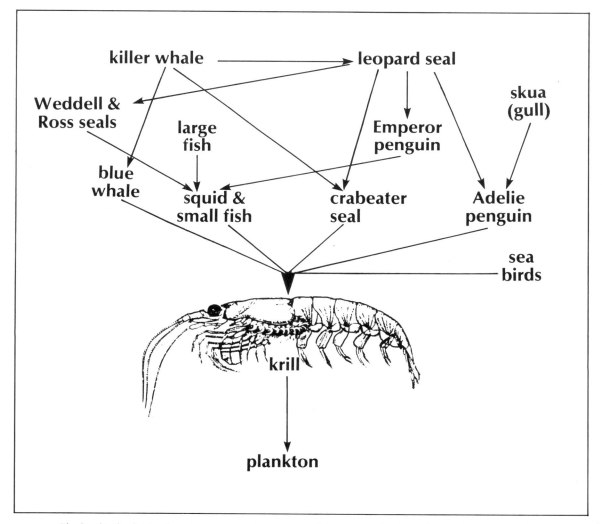

The food web. The Southern Ocean ecosystem is a remarkable one for the dependence of so many species on just one animal — krill.

Alaskan pollack the highest at 5.1 million tonnes. Quite aside from the risks of over-fishing, the very presence of harvesting and processing vessels in the Southern Ocean must have some considerable effect on the environment. It has been estimated that to harvest just over 10 million tonnes, a fleet of 500 large trawlers plus supporting vessels would be required. Such numbers would mean a certain increase in rubbish, pollution and the occurrence of oil spills from the ships.

The list of countries seriously interested or involved in krill fishing is not large, restricted only to those with deep-sea fishing fleets. Besides the Soviet Union, Japan and Poland, sustained interest has been expressed only by East and West Germany, Chile and South Korea. Both East and West Germany attended the Canberra Convention meeting although neither was at that time a full consultative member of the Antarctic Treaty. South Korea, a non-member, showed an interest in attending the Convention, but the Russians objected to its being invited.

The Japanese interest in krill stems from their traditional dependence on seafood, with rising consumer prices and demand sending the Japanese fishing fleets further and further afield. But in the expanding krill fishery, economic returns are not necessarily the guiding factor. Political and strategic considerations also have a bearing on development, especially in the centrally planned economies of Eastern Europe.

Polish krill fishing ventures have been prompted by both the pressure of a chronic protein shortage and the need to redeploy a fairly new fishing fleet being foreclosed on by the new maritime zones in the Northern Hemisphere. A Southern Ocean fishery that returns only a reasonable proportion of operating costs can appear attractive when one considers the alternative: the high costs of redundancy of both fishing fleets and workers. As has been mentioned, the enormous Russian fleet is under similar pressure and Soviet interest in krill as stock feed could intensify if their supplies of North American grain are threatened by political action.

It should be stressed that the objective of any fishery's management is not only to prevent damage to the environment by carefully regulating commercial harvesting to a safe level, but also to prevent economic losses to the fishing industry from over-investment and over-development. The continuing struggle to save the baleen whales from extermination through the diplomatic channels of the IWC demonstrates how easy it is for economic interests to oppose all regulation once an industry is under way.

Present krill catches are around 200,000 tonnes per season and, fortunately for the krill, a bonanza fishery on the Southern Ocean within a few years now seems doubtful. Although certain difficulties have been overcome in the last few years, other developments suggest that the krill fishery will grow quite slowly.

The rapid rise in fuel costs in the late 1970s has helped defer the marine harvests, particularly by those Northern Hemisphere states whose fleets must travel thousands of kilometres each year for a season of only three months or so. Although new fishing methods have led to higher catch rates since 1976, catches of 120 tonnes per day — the maximum possible with existing technology — must be sustained for the whole length of the season if even current operating costs are to be recovered.

Work on product development has progressed significantly since 1977, but market problems still exist. The future of krill as a food for humans is now suspect, judging by recent Norwegian and American studies on the fluoride levels. The Norwegians T. Soevik and O.R. Braekkan found in 1979 that ground krill contains fluoride levels seven to 24 times higher than those permitted by the U.S. Food and Drug Administration. [3]

A report prepared by the International Institute for Environment and Development in 1980 indicates that market constraints are also acting on krill fishery expansion. According to the report, krill are likely to remain a high quality, low-volume product, and higher operating expenses mean that krill will probably be unable to compete with more traditional — and accessible — sources for fish-meal and protein concentrates. At the most, krill could capture 10 per cent of the world market by 1985, but this is an optimistic projection. [4]

At whatever its rate of development, however, the krill fishery on the Southern Ocean will need to be closely monitored.

NOTES

1. See I. Everson, *The Living Resources of the Southern Ocean* (FAO Report), 1977.
2. *Dominion*, 14 Feb 81.
3. O.R. Braekkan and T. Soevik, "Fluoride in Antarctic Krill and Atlantic Krill" in *Journal of Fisheries Research Board* (Canada), Nov 1979.
4. B. Mitchell and R. Sandbrook, *The Management of the Southern Ocean*, International Institute for Environment and Development, London, 1980.

Chapter 7

COMMERCE ON THE SOUTHERN OCEAN

Despite its remoteness, the Southern Ocean has a long history of commercial harvesting. Regrettably, several countries have continued to eye the economic potential of two mammals which have suffered in the past from gross exploitation — whales and seals. The commercial possibilities of other Southern Ocean species such as fin fish, crustaceans and squid, have also been attracting attention.

For over 60 years from the turn of the century, Antarctic waters were the world's major whaling grounds. Baleen and sperm whales came south every summer to feed in the rich waters, increasing their weight by as much as 50 per cent to cover leaner times further north. The whales were hunted principally for their oil, a product valued not only as a fine lubricant for industry, but also for other commercial applications in leatherwork and cosmetics. Further, whale meat has been a traditional food item, particularly in Japan.

It was the advent of large factory ships, with stern slipways and rendering decks, which enabled the systematic devastation of the whales. Until the late 1920s, shore-based stations had meant that only restricted areas of ocean could be worked, for there was a limit to the distances that harpooned whales could be towed for processing.

Early whaling, from a sketch by Gordon Grant. Dramatic inroads on world whale populations only became possible after the 1860s with the invention of the explosive harpoon gun and the development of ships able to catch the faster-moving whale species. For over 60 years from the turn of the century the Southern Ocean was the world's premier whaling ground. *Canterbury Museum*

By the 1930s, however, Southern Ocean whaling had become an onslaught, and over the next 20 years (excluding the war years), between 30,000 and 45,000 whales were taken each season. Concerted conservation action prompted an international attempt to regulate the whaling, but the resulting convention of 1935 was a complete failure. It adopted the expedient of setting catch quotas in terms of Blue Whale Units (BWU) [1], but this only made it more efficient to fill a quota with as many of the larger whales as possible, and the destruction of whale stocks was hastened rather than hindered. As the blue whale — the largest and most profitable — became scarce, whalers concentrated on the fin and sperm whales, and then on the smaller sei and minke whales as each stock

in turn was depleted to uneconomic levels.

In 1946 the convention was re-established in the form of the International Whaling Commission (IWC) to regulate "the orderly development of the whaling industry". This, too, has been an abject failure, operating from insufficient data and unheeded scientific advice. The history of the IWC has been one of repeated claims by the whaling nations that adequate information existed to ensure that their suggested quotas were safe, followed consistently by the discovery that the quotas determined were too high and that whale populations were being depleted.

Only when whale stocks slumped to dangerously low levels did the whaling

The *Kyo Maru*, a Japanese whale catcher berthed at Wellington in February 1981. Along with two other catchers, one Japanese and one Russian, the vessel had just completed a two-month survey of whale populations in Antarctic waters at the behest of the IWC. The expedition leader was reported to have been surprised at the small number of whales spotted during the survey. *Bill Wieben*

A minke whale surfaces. With an average length of less than 10 metres, the minke is the smallest of the baleen whales: until other whale populations reached critically low levels it was not considered worth catching. The whale is hunted for its meat, primarily for pet food and the Japanese delicatessen market; the IWC quota for Southern Ocean minkes in the 1981-82 season was 6,700. *Ray Goldring*

nations give any serious attention to effective quotas and restrictions. The Blue Whale Unit was abolished in 1972, but the annual quotas were still regularly decided mainly on the basis of economic and political considerations. The advice of the Commission's scientific committee on the whales' natural replacement rates and other matters were routinely ignored.

The IWC has been manifestly unable — and unwilling — to prevent the decline of whales, and the cruel slaughter of these highly intelligent mammals continued until numbers were almost too low to make hunting worthwhile. By the mid-1960s whalers had begun to shift the hunt for large whales to the less ravaged North Pacific, and the remaining Norwegian shore station at South Georgia closed down in 1964.

No one knows whether the baleen whale populations will ever recover to their former sizes, or even if some will be saved from extinction. Dr Peter Best, the

chief scientist for the recent survey of whale numbers in the Southern Ocean, saw far fewer whales than he had expected. The numbers reported to the IWC revealed just how sadly depleted the Antarctic whale populations have become. [2] (See chart p. 82.)

At present, blue whale stocks stand at less than five per cent of the original population size. The stock of humpback whales is about three per cent of its initial size, while fin whale stocks are fewer than 20 per cent of their pre-1900 numbers. Sperm whales have declined to about half their original population. As the population of each baleen species has decreased, other changes have happily combined to increase the growth rate of that population. Sexual maturity among baleen whales is now reached at a younger age than when stocks were larger, and the pregnancy rate is also increasing.

At the United Nations Conference on the Human Environment in 1972, 100 nations adopted a resolution calling for a 10-year moratorium on whaling. Conservationists within the IWC (including Australia and New Zealand) have made repeated calls for the moratorium to be implemented, but Japan and the Soviet Union have strenuously opposed such a move.

There are only two IWC countries still actively whaling on the Southern Ocean. In recent summers, one Japanese and two Russian factory ships, with 34 catcher boats between them, have continued to operate south of the Antarctic Convergence. Japanese efforts are concentrated on the minke whale — a species once considered too small to be worth hunting. Minkes are sought primarily for their meat, although this now has only a very small part in the Japanese diet. The Japanese

whaling catch for 1980-81 amounted to 12,845 tonnes of frozen meat and 1,740 tonnes of whale oil. Whale meat has been used as pet food in some Western countries, but the European Economic Community banned the importation of all whale products into member countries in 1980.

Although the Russians also hunt minkes, exporting the meat to Japan or using it for mink-farming (ironically), sperm whales have been their major target. In 1981, however, a ban on sperm whale hunting was passed at that year's Commission meeting. In any event, current research on the jojoba bean indicates a promising alternative source of oil, refuting the Russian contention that sperm oil is indispensable in certain industrial processes. Jojoba grows naturally

With only their dorsal fins and shiny backs showing, a small herd of killer whales (orcas) momentarily surface in the ship channel of McMurdo Sound. The whales are very curious about the Navy icebreakers and cargo ships that travel the channel to McMurdo Station. In mid summer, these whales can also be seen in Winter Quarters Bay at the foot of McMurdo Station. *Official US Navy photograph*

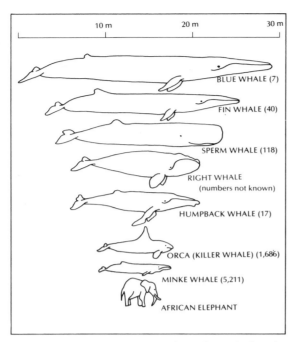

 gives scale bar: 10 m, 20 m, 30 m.

BLUE WHALE (7)

FIN WHALE (40)

SPERM WHALE (118)

RIGHT WHALE
(numbers not known)

HUMPBACK WHALE (17)

ORCA (KILLER WHALE) (1,686)

MINKE WHALE (5,211)

AFRICAN ELEPHANT

Southern Ocean whale species, with an African elephant for comparison. Numbers given in brackets indicate the number of whales of each species counted during a two-month population survey in Antarctic waters in early 1981.
Greenpeace/Angela Bodley

in the deserts of Mexico and the south-west United States, and oil from the beans has similar properties to those of whale oil, with the added advantage of being odourless. Trial jojoba plantations are already underway in California.

Both the Japanese and Russian whalers employ helicopters, spotter planes and a type of sonar in the search for their quarry, but their returns, relative to effort, are steadily diminishing. Despite this, the annual Antarctic quota for minkes was increased to 8102 at the 1981 Commission meeting. The fins, blues, humpbacks and southern right whales are totally protected in the Southern Ocean, though not from the pirate whalers who have been operating in recent years. These pirate whalers have received technical assistance and equipment from the Japanese, Norwegians and the South Africans, while commercial outlets have been provided by Korea and Japan (through the multinational Taiyo fishing company).

As the numbers of sei and minke whales progressively decline, attention will be turned to the smaller cetaceans. In 1979 the Russians reported killing 916 orcas (killer whales) in Antarctic waters. These are quite small whales, and a major struggle may ensue in the IWC about whether their kind are legally included in its jurisdiction. That the Commission has never managed to agree on what is, or is not, a "whale" is an indication of its ineffectiveness.

The progress of the IWC towards scientifically based quotas and sanctuaries has been slow and irksome. The objections of the Japanese stymied the attempt at the 1980 Commission meeting to have the newly created Indian Ocean Sanctuary extend right to the Antarctic pack ice, and its southern limit was set at 55°S.

While the IWC's broad constituency now includes a slim majority of conservation-oriented states, its decisions are binding only to the extent of each member country's willingness to co-operate. Violations of its quotas have been frequent, yet the Commission is powerless to act upon them. As one observer to the 1980 meeting in Brighton wryly commented: "The Infractions Committee has no teeth — it doesn't even have gums."

Internal pressures within the IWC have sharpened since 1979 with calls for a moratorium on commercial whaling and for tighter controls on the trade in whale products. Voting blocs of the opposing exploitationist countries have become more entrenched, however, and decisions more difficult. The IWC Secretariat concedes that internal disputes could tear the Commission apart, leaving unsupervised whaling as a consequence.

In 1981 Canada announced its withdrawal from the Commission, after intense domestic politicking over quotas for non-commercial Eskimo whale hunting. At previous meetings the country had incensed conservationists by voting with the commercial whaling nations, much to the embarrassment of the Canadian Foreign Office.

With or without IWC control, it seems that whaling on the Southern Ocean will, despite diminishing returns, continue for as long as the market demands.

Of the six species of seal found within the Antarctic regions, the crabeater, leopard, Weddell and Ross seals have been subject to commercial exploitation on only two occasions. In 1964, the Norwegian ship *Polarhav* worked the pack ice on an experimental expedition for the crabeater seal, the most abundant Antarctic species. In two months the expedition killed 1,127 seals, but finding their quarry in the pack ice was apparently too slow, too difficult and too uneconomic for further expeditions to be undertaken. The Russians took 1,000 seals experimentally in 1972, but presumably to little economic advantage. They have not been back for more.

Weddell seals are used to feed the several dog teams that are still retained at some Antarctic bases. Although the number of Weddells killed for dog food is trivial compared with the total population, killings have dented local communities. At Scott Base in McMurdo Sound it was found that between 1956 and 1960 the local harvest of Weddell seals was so heavy that it depressed the number of pups born in the area for several years. Only with new rules and restrictions has the seal population slowly recovered.

The elephant and fur seals of the subantarctic islands have not escaped so lightly and several times have been hunted to near extinction. On South Georgia alone 1.2 million fur seals were killed in the periods 1780-1830 and 1860-80. When the sealer Nathaniel Palmer and Captain Thaddeus Bellingshausen met by chance in the South Shetlands in 1821, Palmer told the Russian that his fleet of sealers had already killed 80,000 seals in the vicinity that season.

Fur seals were hunted for their valuable pelts, while elephant seals were killed for their oil. Male elephant seals were cropped on a sustainable yield basis at South Georgia until 1964 and as recently as the early 1970s in the Kerguelen archipelago.

The Convention for the Conservation of Antarctic Seals came into force in 1978, and protects these two species as long as they are south of 60°S. On the advice of biologists, the Ross seal is also totally protected, while quotas have been established for the crabeater, leopard and Weddell seals. The Convention also allows for a sealing commission, scientific and advisory bodies, open and closed areas and seasons, and a proper record of all animals killed. The seals must also be killed quickly and humanely, and are to be hunted only on land.

There appears to be no interest in commercial sealing in the Southern Ocean at present and, with protection, the fur seal numbers have recovered from about 100 in the 1930s to 15,000 in 1954, and 350,000 in 1976. These increases seem to be tied partly to a greater availability of krill following the demise of the baleen whales.

Penguins were once exploited for their oil — a mere half-litre per bird — on subantarctic Macquarie Island. In 1895 Joseph Hatch of Invercargill, New Zealand, set up rendering works there, and boiled down 150,000 King penguins each year until, in 1919, amidst wide public indignation at such gratuitous slaughter, the Tasmanian Government refused further licences. Contrary to popular opinion, the birds were not marched into the vats and boiled alive, but were at least killed the night before.

While the waters of the Southern Ocean produce a wealth of plankton, there is no correspondingly large fish population. In contrast to other oceans, there are no dense shoals of pelagic fish in Antarctic waters. The Southern Ocean is between 4,000 and 5,000 metres deep in most places, and there are only limited areas of shallow water. Unlike the extensive Arctic continental shelves, where fish are found in abundance, the Antarctic continental shelf is generally narrow and unusually deep. Thus only about 100 of the 20,000 or so fish species found in the earth's oceans have been identified south of the Antarctic Convergence.

Of these 100 species, only three or four appear to be of commercial interest, either for their individual size or numbers. Antarctic cod, icefish and Patagonian hake have been trawled since 1970 but precise catch information is lacking. Fish stocks around South Georgia and Kerguelen have been the target of extensive fishing by the Russians, who caught 417,000 tonnes of fish around South Georgia in 1970. Very low yields for the following years indicate that the area had been quickly overfished and confirm once again that immediate economic interests invariably overrule sound fisheries management.

Present signs are that the three East European fishing states (the Soviet Union, East Germany and Poland) are again increasing their Antarctic fin fish catch. The total catch of fin fish reported to the FAO for 1977 was 279,000 tonnes, which compares with a reported krill catch of 122,000 tonnes. Russian trawlers have taken fish catches of up to 40,000 tonnes annually around Kerguelen for some years. The French won an exclusion of their Kerguelen and Crozet submarine shelves from the Marine Resources Convention jurisdiction, and have since established a 370-kilometre economic zone around the shelves. Under a quota payment arrangement, Russian and Polish trawlers continue to fish there, and the French themselves have begun to investigate the commercial prospects more closely. French deepwater fishing and marketing organisations spent $NZ2 million on an experimental cruise around the Kerguelen and Crozet archipelagos in 1979 and further exploration is in the offing. Australian commercial interests are also reported to be examining the fishing potential of the subantarctic, around Macquarie and Heard Islands.

A number of other countries including West Germany, Japan and Argentina, are believed to be evaluating the potential of Antarctic fish. The Russians have also shown interest in southern blue whiting, one of the very few fish species to make a seasonal crossing of the Antarctic Convergence. Southern blue whiting is a prime species found around the Campbell Plateau, a major subantarctic fishing ground within New Zealand's 370-kilometre maritime zone. According to the Ministry of Agriculture and Fisheries, which carefully monitors all foreign fishing in New Zealand waters, the Russian catch of whiting from the area over 1979/80 was 23,000 tonnes.

In 1975, three biologists at the United States National Marine Fisheries Service suggested the establishment of an Antarctic salmon fishery, using Atlantic salmon fry. The biologists proposed that the fry be introduced to the rivers and streams of southern Argentina, Chile and the Kerguelen Islands. The salmon would feed on krill during the marine phase of their life cycle, and would be trapped on their return to the home streams to spawn — as they are in the Arctic and subarctic.

The French appear to have taken this idea seriously, as each season since 1977 they have transplanted salmon fry from their Kerguelen hatchery to the streams of Crozet Island. It is yet too soon to tell if a run has been established, but it is an innovation of considerable interest. Salmon have been the world's most important canning fish since 1824, but in the Northern Hemisphere they have, predictably, been overfished. Harvesting the fish on their return from the sea eliminates the huge fuel costs which face ocean-going fisheries.

The commercial potential of the Southern Ocean squid, rock lobsters, crabs and other invertebrates has hardly been explored. The French took 5,000 tonnes of lobsters from the Kerguelen Shelf for a few seasons until the rapid decline in the catch gave some clues to their sparse populations. Experimental harvests conducted by the French in the mid-1970s for stone crabs around the Crozet Islands resulted in large catches and further surveys are continuing. A joint New Zealand-Japanese expedition located a sizable population of spider crabs at the Auckland Islands and at the Pukaki Rise on the New Zealand subantarctic shelf. Fisheries scientists Ryff and Voller estimated a possible annual harvest approaching 500,000 crabs. [3] There is little in the way of commercial shellfish in Antarctic waters.

Squid are thought to be very numerous, but knowledge of their biology and habits is very limited. Their populations are difficult to sample, as they are strong swimmers and elude nets, but it is estimated that they make up a substantial proportion — perhaps 20 per cent — of the biomass of the Southern Ocean. Squid form the major diet of sperm whales and are an important source of food for seals, fish and some sea birds. Several species of squid have actually never been found alive or intact but have been determined to be new species solely from the features of their beaks which, being indigestible, are regurgitated by albatrosses near their nests.

There is no Antarctic squid fishery at present, but ocean squid fishing near New Zealand (over 100 boats) and South America could readily expand southwards to the Southern Ocean. The Japanese are certainly interested in the possibilities for Antarctic squid. A squid fishery in the Southern Ocean could develop as a sideline to krill and fin fishing in the area, though with the same risks of overfishing and local pollution.

International interest in the marine potential of Antarctic waters has intensified over the last 10 years. There have been calls from Third World countries, in addition to FAO proposals, for an equitable share in the Southern Ocean fisheries.

The Sri Lankan delegate to the Law of the Sea Conference in 1977, Ambassador Pinto, warned that Antarctic fisheries should not become the subject of "selfish and irresponsible exploitation by those who for the time being possess the technology for the purpose".

But the distribution of resources to the world did not form part of the Marine Living Resources Convention negotiations. Nevertheless, it is quite apparent that the problems of the Third World that could be alleviated to some degree by Antarctic krill exploitation would be better solved by spending far more money and expertise on remedies for present environmental and food production ills. Deforestation, overgrazing, desertification, erosion and overfishing are all problems for which solutions must be found, but which the extensive capital investment necessary for krill fishing would scarcely solve. Nutrition gained from the Southern Ocean is unlikely to be used for those who most need it.

Pinto's admonition reflects the prevailing belief among international bodies — and particularly those dominated by Third World countries — in the concept of the global commons, and the Sri Lankan concern has far-reaching implications. The protracted Law of the Sea conferences have had as a major aim the resolution of ownership of the mineral resources of the deep-sea floor: that its resources and revenues should be fairly shared out. Many Third World states have made it clear that both the marine and mineral resources of Antarctica must be considered from a similar perspective.

The Marine Living Resources Convention does not acknowledge the interests of the wider international community beyond those states which are either members of the Antarctic Treaty or who already possess the technology to exploit krill and Antarctic fish. The Chileans, for example, were completely against allowing Third World countries access to Southern Ocean marine resources. Major

Third World fishing nations such as Taiwan and the two Koreas are permitted to accede to the Convention provisions, but were not given a look-in at its negotiations. Although from an environmentalists point of view this exclusion was probably a good thing, the Convention cannot prevent non-members from fishing or from ignoring Convention rules.

In part, the Convention was the Antarctic Club's response to outside initiatives from United Nations, organisations and conservationists to broaden political participation in the Antarctic. The Treaty members have always been anxious to retain their collective control over Antarctic affairs. Confidential telexes exchanged between the Australian Foreign Ministry and its Argentine and Sri Lankan ambassadors, since leaked to the conservationist press, testify to this determination to stall internationalist initiatives. [4]

In 1975, the Director of the United Nations Environment Programme (UNEP) called for a moratorium on Antarctic development, and a proposal to extend the political base of the Antarctic Treaty was made. Consideration was blocked by the Treaty powers, however. The 1977 FAO proposal for a $45 million, 10-year programme to "explore, exploit and utilise" the living resources of the Southern Ocean for the benefit of the whole world was similarly opposed, and was finally withdrawn after pressure from the Antarctic Treaty powers.

The Treaty powers had in fact already commenced, through SCAR, their own research programme, and the 10-year BIOMASS programme is now under way. A joint project between SCAR and SCOR (Scientific Committee on Oceanographic Research), the scientific focus of BIOMASS is on krill, and should supply invaluable data for the marine convention. Many other species besides krill are being studied, together with research on Antarctic currents, vertical mixing of ocean water and pack-ice distribution. Observations will be made by remote-sensing satellite and from 20 research vessels and shore stations of all the major countries involved in Antarctic research.

The main observational periods of BIOMASS are 1980-81 and 1983-84. The project is the first large interdisciplinary and international programme in the Antarctic, and the breadth of its survey reveals how little is known about the Southern Ocean and its inhabitants.

NOTES

1. "The Blue Whale Unit completely ignored the natural peculiarities of each species by lumping all baleen whales together as so many different sized containers of oil." (CIA *Polar Regions Atlas*, p.52.) Depending on the number of barrels of oil produced by an average-sized whale of a particular species, one BWU was set at either one blue, two fins, three humpbacks, five seis, or any equivalent combination. Even then, the IWC allowed member nations to free themselves from quota limits by simply rejecting them. It still does.
2. *Dominion*, 14 Feb 81.
3. M.R. Ryff, and R.W. Voller, *Fisheries Technical Report* No.143, 1976.
4. See *Ice*, No.5, 16 May 1980, Antarctic Defence Coalition (Australia).

Chapter 8

BLACK AND WHITE PROSPECTS

Future historians of the human race will marvel at our civilisation's total dependence on petroleum. In not much more than a century, since Drake's first well gushed forth in the Pennsylvanian backwoods in 1859, the economies and foreign policies of nations have come to pivot on its steady supply.

The manner in which the world has become blindly hooked on oil is like the drug dependence of a heroin addict (though we never read about it in the *Reader's Digest*). Western civilisation cruises from fix to fix, howling at every OPEC attempt to wean it from the habit while searching desperately for submarine "opium" fields of its own.

Not surprisingly then, interest in Antarctica as a potential source of oil has increased as more accessible reserves elsewhere have been consumed by the relentless appetites of the industrial societies. Antarctica's potential mineral resources have been estimated largely by what can be inferred from its geological similarities with other Gondwana continents, yet the hint of oil on the continental shelf has resounded through cabinet rooms and oil company board rooms worldwide in recent years.

The extraction of Antarctic minerals in the harsh extremes of the polar environ-ment may have questionable economic viability, but the colossal disruption and injury that exploitation could impose on the fragile Antarctic ecosystems is beyond doubt, given that only large-scale operations could be profitable. The entire continent would be at risk.

Oil has been at the forefront of all discussions of Antarctica's probable mineral resources. The landmass itself is not considered to be a likely source of oil, as the coastal areas of ice-free rock are either too ancient or unsuitable to allow the retention of oil and gas; the inland nunataks are also unsuitable as oil traps.

But the circumstantial evidence for oil and gas existing on the submarine continental shelves is fairly impressive, particularly for the Ross Sea and Weddell Sea Basins. The Ross Sea continental shelf was once adjacent to Bass Strait, between Tasmania and Australia, where oil fields have already been discovered. United States research ships have found thick layers of unmetamorphosed Tertiary sediments in the Ross, Weddell and Bellingshausen Seas, and such sediments are frequently associated with oil. In the Ross Sea region the McMurdo Sound Sediments and Tectonics Study, a New Zealand project aimed at a more accurate dating of the uplift of the Transantarctic

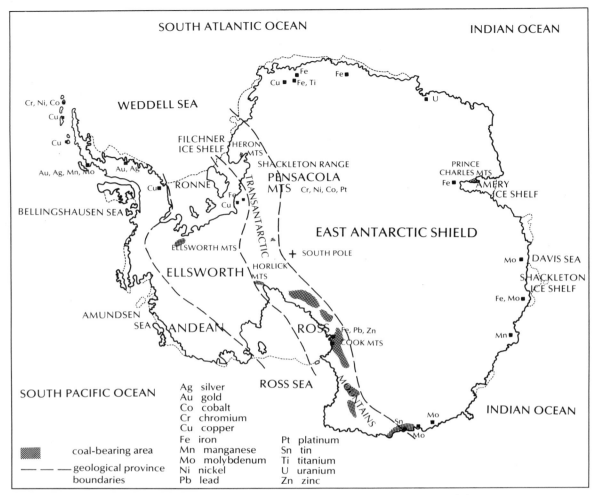

SOUTH ATLANTIC OCEAN   INDIAN OCEAN

WEDDELL SEA

Cr, Ni, Co
Cu

Cu

Au, Ag, Mn, Mo   Au, Ag

BELLINGSHAUSEN SEA

FILCHNER
ICE SHELF   HERON
MTS

SHACKLETON RANGE

PENSACOLA
MTS   Cr, Ni, Co, Pt

RONNE

TRANSANTARCTIC

Cu

Cu

ELLSWORTH MTS

EAST ANTARCTIC SHIELD

Fe
Cu   Fe, Ti   Fe

U

PRINCE
CHARLES MTS
Fe   AMERY
ICE SHELF

Mo   DAVIS SEA

SHACKLETON
ICE SHELF

Fe, Mo

+ SOUTH POLE

ELLSWORTH   HORLICK
MTS

AMUNDSEN
SEA   ANDEAN   ROSS   Fe, Pb, Zn
COOK MTS

MOUNTAINS

Mn

SOUTH PACIFIC OCEAN

Ag silver
Au gold
Co cobalt
Cr chromium
Cu copper
Fe iron
Mn manganese
Mo molybdenum
Ni nickel
Pb lead

ROSS SEA

Sn   Mo
Mo

INDIAN OCEAN

Pt platinum
Sn tin
Ti titanium
U   uranium
Zn zinc

▓ coal-bearing area
— — — geological province
boundaries

Known mineral occurences in Antarctica's four geological provinces. An occurence is by no means an indication of economic feasibility.

Mountains, has added to the overall geological picture favourable to oil exploration. The Ross Sea continental shelf has a high regional heat flow which allows hydrocarbons to develop at relatively shallow depths, and its geological structure is favourably simple, with few faults.

These suspicions were partly confirmed by the geographical and geophysical work of the United States research ship *Glomar Challenger* in 1972-73. The ship drilled 28 holes around the continent, including four in the Ross Sea in water around 600 metres deep. The sites were chosen to

avoid the most likely oil-bearing structures because the ship was not equipped to deal with an oil blow-out. Nevertheless, in three of the Ross Sea holes the hydrocarbons ethane, methane and ethylene were found. These may be evidence for the presence of petroleum hydrocarbons. Methane is common in deep-sea cores, but ethylene often occurs with petroleum.

This event caused a flurry of excitement around the oil world, and prompted the *Wall Street Journal* to send a staff reporter to McMurdo the following Antarctic season to investigate oil prospects on the spot. Until exploratory drilling takes place, however, there is insufficient data to permit any meaningful estimates of the size of potential Antarctic oil and gas reserves. Despite this, estimates based on quite unproven information and of dubious methodology have been widely quoted. The United States Geological Survey report in 1974 calculated the recoverable oil reserves of the Ross, Weddell and Bellingshausen Seas as 15 billion barrels. In 1979 a representative of Gulf Oil stated that the oil potential of the two most likely areas in the Ross and Weddell Seas was in the range of 50 billion barrels, but possibly much more. By comparison, the North Slope oilfield of Alaska is believed to contain eight billion barrels of oil.

The western continental shelf of Antarctica is also estimated to contain vast quantities of gas, but so far attention has concentrated on oil rather than gas. Because it has to be liquified under pressure, the transport costs of natural gas are much higher than those of oil and present energy prices are far too low to support its exploitation in Antarctica.

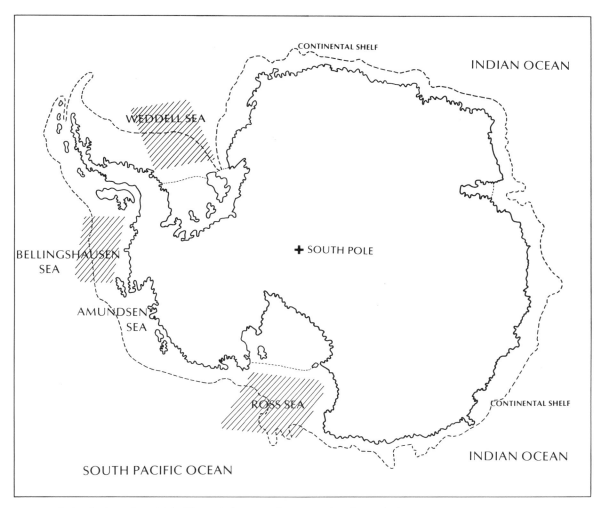

Antarctica's continental shelf is much deeper and narrower than those of other continents. The dotted line marks depths of 1,000 metres around the continent; hatched areas are those to be seismically surveyed by the Japanese during 1980-83, with petroleum prospects as their chief motivation.

There are four stages in the exploration-exploitation process. The first involves regional scientific surveys; the second, intensive local surveys including seismic testing. All current research in the Antarctic is ostensibly purely scientific and non-commercial, but a strong degree of commercial motivation seems far more likely as far as oil is concerned, with prospecting obviously implying a desire to exploit. Exploratory drilling and production drilling are the third and fourth stages — and the environmentally threatening ones.

A special committee of SCAR was set up in 1977 to consider the possibilities and implications of oil exploration in Antarctica. The group of specialists on the Environmental Impact Assessment of Mineral Resource Exploration and Exploitation (EAMREA) reported that the exploration for and exploitation of hydrocarbons in the Antarctic seemed likely to become technically feasible at some time, but estimates of the probable time-scale varied. There was a wide divergence of views amongst the experts. None believed that exploratory drilling would begin within five years, and most of the experts considered that it would be unlikely in less than 10 years. The timetable for exploitation is even more uncertain, but in the much less exacting conditions of the North Sea there was a 10-year gap between exploratory drilling and the flow of oil to the mainland. In Arctic Canada exploratory drilling is well under way, with full-scale production scheduled for 1990.

There is already substantial interest in the search for Antarctic oil. As early as 1969, the Governments of the United States, Australia and New Zealand were approached by commercial interests for prospecting rights in Antarctica. In that year, New Zealand received an application to explore, prospect and develop a large area of the Ross Dependency, and in 1970 Texaco asked the United States Government how to obtain a licence for oil exploration in the Atlantic section of the Antarctic. Texaco was told it could not be issued a licence by the United States Government and was instructed not to ask any other.

Several other major United States oil companies have expressed interest since then, Gulf Oil in particular. Gulf was reported to have had a seismic survey ship working in the South Georgia area in 1979-80, and the company has made proposals for joint survey ventures between government and private interests. At the end of 1978 the United States Gulf Research and Development Company suggested a marine geophysical study of the geology and resources of the Antarctic continental shelves to be jointly sponsored by the National Science Foundation and a consortium of multinationals and foreign governments, to the tune of $US2.5 million per season. Gulf has been prepared to make its seismic ship available and has said it would allow the information gathered to be publicly available. As a global strategy, Gulf "is raising cash to carry out the huge programme of exploration that alone will ensure its survival as a leading force in the world's oil supply". [1] The company is apparently struggling financially, with net profits for 1980 a mere 15 per cent up on those for 1979. (The average increase in net profit for the big oil companies in 1980 was about 44 per cent over that for 1979.)

The oil companies are not without influence within the Western Treaty governments. French delegations to the biennial consultative meetings have included several oil company representatives, and British Petroleum has also been represented there. The Antarctic Advisory Committee of the United States Department of State currently has representatives from the Atlantic Richfield, Gulf and Esso oil companies.

It is likely that American oil companies would consider immediate prospecting along Antarctica's continental margins if their government would guarantee political backing. The Americans have a virtual monopoly on the necessary technical expertise, but are naturally wary of investing millions of dollars in exploratory ventures without the assurance of some internationally accepted legal regime. The Antarctic Treaty has no stipulations to cover mineral exploitation and its jurisdiction over activities on the continental shelves is legally dubious.

The matter of minerals exploitation was first discussed informally among the Treaty nations in 1970. Consultative meetings in 1972 and 1975 considered a minerals regime, but the need for a marine living resources convention was more pressing. For the meantime, the Treaty powers made an informal agreement to discourage any commercial activity connected with possible Antarctic oil until a regime was concluded. At the 1979 meeting in Washington D.C., the Treaty nations tabled a motion to establish a mineral resources regime, but the intricacies of the political settlements and compromises will take a great effort in diplomacy and negotiation. The issue of sovereign claims cannot be skirted in the same way as has been done in the Marine Living Resources Convention.

Nevertheless, the scientific surveys for hydrocarbons now being undertaken by the Japanese, West Germans and Americans will lend considerable momentum to the minerals regime negotiations. The Americans are engaged in regional surveys, and an investigation of the hydrocarbon possibilities along the continental margins of the Bellingshausen Sea was a feature of their 1980-81 Antarctic programme. West Germany had the sophisticated seismic ship *Explora* surveying the Ross Sea region in 1979-80, a project that went unnoticed by the international press.

In 1979 Japan announced plans for a three-year survey for oil and natural gas off the Antarctic continent, using the 1,800-tonne vessel *Hakurei Maru*. The Japanese Government set aside about $NZ2.6 million for the 1980-81 Bellingshausen Sea survey, and commissioned the Japan National Oil Corporation, a government agency, to undertake the work. Further surveys were planned for the Weddell and Ross Seas in 1981-82 and 1982-83 respectively. The Japanese programme is a heavy and very detailed one, and is clearly resource-oriented: "The *Hakurei Maru* will do bottom sampling, depth sounding, and seismic reflections, sono-radio buoy refraction, magnetometer and gravimeter surveys as well as measuring terrestrial heat flows at three points in the Bellingshausen Sea". [2] With further exploration plans in mind, the Japanese are seriously considering the construction of another ice-strengthened research vessel.

The French have also become keen to establish the oil potential of the Kerguelen Shelf, and the state-controlled oil company, Societé Nationale Elf Aquitaine, has applied for a licence for preliminary prospecting for hydrocarbons in the region.

The legal and political aspects of an Antarctic mineral resources regime will be discussed later. Of much greater importance than the diplomatic wranglings will be the Treaty nations' ability to come to grips with the environmental threat of mineral exploitation. Oil is the key focus of the regime negotiations, but there is no doubt that the exploitation of oil in Antarctic waters would have disastrous ecological consequences. The natural hazards and technical difficulties are very great indeed, and could only be compounded by the inevitable factors of human error and equipment failure. Some commentators have said that Antarctic oil extraction would present no greater problems than those now being tackled in Arctic oil development, but the comparison is only a superficial one. The Antarctic ice environment has important differences, and there are further difficulties with the continent's inaccessibility and its remoteness from industrial centres and transport networks.

Exploratory drilling for Antarctic oil would be a tough venture. Unlike production drilling it, at least, could be

Weathering produces strange shapes on Antarctic icebergs. Depending on its shape, up to six-sevenths of an iceberg is under water. The expression "the tip of the iceberg" is not used in this book, but the colossal scale of Antarctic icebergs would pose an extreme hazard for any hydrocarbon exploitation on the continental shelf. *Antarctic Division, DSIR*

done as a self-contained operation without the need for any land bases — although the Antarctic seas have open water for only two or three months of the year. Outside this short season, they are covered by pack ice — broken but continuous ice up to 1.5 metres thick which moves with the winds as much as 65 kilometres per day. Within the pack ice are immense tabular bergs calved from the ice shelves. While south of 60°S wind velocities generally decrease, sudden storms on the coastal seas can spring without warning, with wind gusts up to 200 kilometres per hour.

The continental shelf around Antarctica is much deeper than that off other continents, having been carved out by the greater glaciations of the last Ice Age. The Ross Sea is up to 800 metres deep in some places, and the seaward edge of the Antarctic continental shelf averages 500 metres below sea level. The technology for deep-sea drilling is advancing rapidly, however. An international scientific workshop held in Italy in 1979 concluded that "It is clear that present technology may already be adequate for exploratory drilling for oil in many parts of the Antarctic seas. The pace of technological advance is such that within five years even more areas will be accessible." [3]

In Arctic Canada, drilling has already been successfully undertaken in continuous summer pack ice two metres thick, and over water 1,500 metres deep. The

Canadian oil company, Dome Petroleum, has now had four seasons' drilling experience in the shallow Beaufort Sea in the Canadian Arctic. Five holes have been drilled, at a cost of $C50 million each, by ice-strengthened ships with the support of ice-breaking tugs. One well, called Kopanoor M-13, has been a major commercial strike, producing 12,000 barrels a day. Dome Petroleum has a further $C200 million budgeted for exploration in the Canadian Arctic over the next few years.

In the iceberg-ridden waters of the Grand Banks off Newfoundland, oil companies have so far drilled 70 exploratory wells. The Hibernia P-15 well has struck a field thought to contain about 1.5 billion barrels of high-grade oil, making it the largest single oil find in North America since Prudhoe Bay in Alaska in the 1960s. But a grim reminder of the region's ice hazards is the fact that the *Titanic* collided with an iceberg and sank not far east of Hibernia.

Advanced technology has also made deep-water drilling practicable. In 1979 Texaco drilled six kilometres into the sea floor 290 kilometres off the Newfoundland coast, in water 1,500 metres deep. The drilling took four months and cost $US35 million, but no hydrocarbons were found. The rig could move off location in the event of icebergs.

The main environmental hazard with exploratory drilling in polar conditions is the risk of a blow-out and the subsequent uncontrolled discharge of oil and gas. Although blow-outs are relatively rare, the precedent of the Bay of Campeche disaster in the Gulf of Mexico in 1979 must not be forgotten. In June 1979, workmen on a semi-submersible rig anchored in the bay had just withdrawn a drill pipe from the well when the heavy drilling mud and water suddenly gushed out, followed by oil and natural gas in an uncontrollable flow. Attempts to stop the flow were unsuccessful and oil flowed from the well for the next 10 months, at rates as high as 40,000 barrels per day. Although the technology needed to halt the flow was close at hand in the United States, it was simply not up to the task. Millions of barrels polluted the gulf and spoiled beaches along the Texan and Mexican coasts. The *New Scientist* reported an oil slick "split into several segments each up to 110 kilometres long, spread over 600 kilometres ... Once it had weathered, portions of the slick would sink, moving along with the current as deep as 12 metres below the surface."[4]

The seriousness of a blow-out in Antarctic seas would be increased by climatic stress and the limited season for drilling operations. The harshness of the climate would increase the risk of human error and of equipment failure. In the extreme conditions steel structures would be more vulnerable to the brittle fracture of welds and steel parts. If a blow-out could not be capped, or a relief well drilled, before the sea ice began to re-form in March, then nothing could be done for at least six months — while the oil steadily gushed out under the pack ice.

Scientists and conservationists have certainly viewed the exploratory drilling in the Canadian Arctic with some disquiet. "Canada's plunge into offshore oil could well be environmental madness," states a *Maclean's* report. "It now appears more certain than ever that pay dirt will be struck long before either industry or government is prepared for the environmental consequences." [5] Government scientists are evidently worried because the technology to clean up a large cold-water spill just does not exist. In the event of a blow-out over winter the oil industry would be powerless to do anything.

The Canadian Government indicated the current lack of knowledge about the effects of oil on ice when, in June 1980, it authorised a series of experimental oil spills off northern Baffin Island, high in the Arctic. The experiments will be part of a five-year, $C4 million project financed by three countries and various multinationals.

The Canadians are developing stringent regulations in an effort to guard against well blow-outs and other mishaps in the Arctic exploration programme. The Government requires two ships to operate in any one area, and drilling must stop at a specified time before the end of the season. Dome Petroleum has both $C60 million in insurance coverage for its Beaufort Sea operations and a $C20 million bond for the Alaskan shoreline. Under Government pressure, the company set its own careful guidelines for Arctic operations — and then disregarded them. It was caught for failing to report 22 minor oil spills in 1979. Dome has also suffered a number of accidents since 1976; these include three high-pressure water and gas blow-outs and two ship spills totalling 295,000 litres of fuel from damaged ice-breaking support vessels.

The exploration for Arctic oil will be watched apprehensively by polar environmentalists. The harmful effects that oil extraction are bound to have on Arctic ecosystems can only be magnified when translated to an Antarctic scenario. Developments in the Canadian Arctic will at least be relatively accessible and under the control of one national government.

The greatest impact of oil exploitation on the Antarctic would be at the production stage. The number of people involved could vary from around 500 in the winter to several thousand in summer — at least doubling Antarctica's present population. Production drilling would require a land base, supposing that an environmentally acceptable onshore site could be found onto the very limited stretches of smooth, ice-free coast. The best onshore sites are already occupied by scientific stations, and many areas already declared wildlife conservation areas under the Antarctic Treaty are on the same coasts. The impact of a land base would be dramatic, involving the construction of ship moorings, pipeline head, oil storage tanks, an airstrip and living quarters for the staff. The recreation activities of oil workers and the

wastes from the base would also have extensive local effects.

Production technology for polar conditions is still in the design stage, but is currently being developed for the oilfields off Newfoundland and the Labrador coast. A production system involving a mobile platform able to process up to 100,000 barrels per day from sea-floor installations has recently been described in the oil industry press. [6] The system is designed for summer operation in water depths of up to 300 metres and in drifting pack ice 1.8 metres thick, and its mobility takes into account million-tonne icebergs drifting by at one kilometre per hour. As iceberg keels can scour the sea floor to some depth as they scrape over it, a scour depth of five metres on the sea floor is allowed for in 300 metres of water. This is less than generous, however, considering that Arctic icebergs have been recorded at 134 metres and 158 metres above the waterline. The draughts of such bergs would easily exceed 300 miles.

In the Antarctic, production drilling at sea would probably be carried out during the summer only, with very large floating platforms, to act as ice-fenders, secured by means of moorings and some form of self-propulsion. The Ross Sea would be the most likely location for oil exploitation, as it is much more accessible by ship than the Bellinghausen or Weddell Seas. Although the Ross Sea is deep, the risk of iceberg scour cannot be ruled out even in water depths of 500 metres. While the immense tabular icebergs have draughts of 180-300 metres, those of dome-shaped icebergs can exceed 400 metres. Thus the well-heads would almost certainly have to be sunk into the sea bed.

The possible environmental impacts of this technology, 10 or 20 years into the future, are extreme. Natural gas, if flared at the platform, would cause air pollution and thus imperil one of the continent's greatest scientific assets. To release the gas at the underwater well-head — another method used by the oil industry — would

The US Navy *Private John R. Towle* moored in the shipping channel in McMurdo Sound. In winter, Antarctic coasts are inaccessible to shipping because the sea ice extends hundreds of kilometres northwards. Even in summer ships must be ice-strengthened or have an icebreaker support, and it is a rare season when a shipping channel to Ross Island need not be driven. Antarctic oil exploitation would thus be confined to the short summer season. *Chris Horne*

be detrimental to Southern Ocean eco-systems to an unknown degree. The natural contamination of Antarctic waters by submarine seepage of crude oil appears to be very low. Unlike the Arctic, petroleum-devouring bacteria have not been noted.

The biggest hazard of all, however, would be an oil spill. This could come from a well blow-out, from ruptured pipelines or tanks, or from a tanker spill.

Icebergs, though not common in the Ross Sea area, would be a formidable problem when encountered. Arctic icebergs are much smaller and can be edged away from drilling rigs by tugs, but Antarctic icebergs are on a different scale: a berg the size of Australian Capital Territory was photographed in 1977 by United States satellites. Whereas pack ice moves

with wind or surface currents, icebergs are moved by the deeper currents and possess enormous momentum.

Production systems for Antarctic conditions would definitely need to be able to detach and move "off location" because it would not be possible to divert a large iceberg if a platform was in its path. In the Arctic attempts have been made to destroy icebergs with bombs, torpedoes, shells and even ramming — quite unsuccessfully. Even with 20 450-kilogram bombs scoring direct hits it was possible to chip away only about one-fifth of a 250,000-tonne iceberg. In the North Atlantic the International Ice Patrol (the *Titanic's* heritage) even tried painting half an iceberg with charcoal to increase heat absorption, but the results were inconclusive.

Surprisingly little is known about the

95

habits of Antarctic icebergs. The Norwegians have tagged icebergs in the Weddell Sea in order to trace their movements, and the British began studying patterns of movement and scour in the 1980-81 season. The gaps in scientific knowledge regarding icebergs are amongst many that must be faced in any attempt to assess in detail the consequences of Antarctic oil exploitation.

But it is not difficult to assess the effects of a large oil spill — only its magnitude is incalculable. A tanker spill would be the most likely hazard. A major oil field (and only a major one would be economically worthwhile) would need one supertanker of 250,000-500,000 tonnes every week. In the Canadian Arctic, Dome Petroleum foresees a fleet of perhaps 20 ice-breaking tankers, each carrying one million barrels of oil once full-scale production is reached. Given Antarctica's gales and storms, icebergs and pack ice, tanker accidents and spills would be unavoidable.

Antarctic supply tankers have already had some close calls. In January 1976 the American supply tanker *Maumee* was very nearly holed when its bow was damaged by ice at the water-line. Steel plating 2.5 centimetres thick was breached in a gash 10 metres long and three metres deep. The *Maumee* was safely double-hulled, but at the time it carried 16 million litres of fuel on board. In 1978 this vessel was actually holed in another accident, but no oil was lost.

The worst tanker oil spill so far in the world has been the 150,000 tonnes spilt by the *Amoco Cadiz* in 1978. But in the Antarctic, rough seas, floating ice and larger

Damage by ice at the waterline of the United States supply tanker *Maumee* demonstrates the risks to which Antarctic oil tankers would be exposed. In February 1976 the *Maumee*'s tanks were very nearly holed while loaded with 16 million litres of fuel. Workmen at Lyttelton here inspect the damage. *Star*

tankers would guarantee worse spills than this. Technological innovations and shipboard sensing equipment may help to reduce the hazards, but the ships would still need human operators. A recent Canadian Government study of oil spills related 78 per cent of them to human error.

The release of a full cargo of oil into the Ross Sea could conceivably affect an area of up to one million square kilometres. Several large spills would be an ecological catastrophe. Antarctic wildlife is more vulnerable than that of any other area because nearly all Antarctic species live on or by the sea: studies persistently report that the animals worst affected by oil spills are those which, like seabirds, regularly move in and out of the water. Penguin and seal colonies would be extremely sensitive to even a small, isolated spill.

Penguin colonies along the South African coast were severely distressed by oil spilled in the collision of two tankers in 1977. Between them, the sister ships *Venoil* and *Venpet* lost over 24 million litres of crude oil and 2.5 million litres of bunker fuel in this accident. In early 1981 about 100,000 seabirds died in an oil spill in Norwegian and Swedish waters. Most of the birds froze to death after their plumage was covered by greasy oil from the slick, and at least 10,000 were shot to end their suffering.

Baleen whales, which feed by straining plankton from large mouthfuls of water, would suffer particularly severely in an Antarctic oil spill. Oil could foul baleen plates or irritate the blowhole; it could damage the eyes and interfere with respiration through the skin. Calves would take in oil while nursing, as would adults while feeding. In the Arctic, the environmental impact audit for the Alaskan offshore lease sales has stated that one major oil spill at the wrong time of year (not that there is any right time of year for an oil spill) could wipe out half the already endangered bowhead whale population of the Beaufort Sea. In any Ross Sea development scenario, the whales most at

risk would be the very species already most endangered: the huge blue and fin whales which graze the closest to the continent.

The Canadians are now undertaking research into the biological effects of oil pollution in Arctic waters with their programme for Eastern Arctic Environmental Studies (EAMES). Scientists with the EAMES project have conducted some rather distasteful experiments into the effects of oil on marine life. These have included a field programme involving the oil-immersion of captive beluga whales, and field and laboratory experiments into the chronic effects of oil ingestion by captive seals and birds. A public uproar in Canada prevented a test on four polar bears from being carried out. The bears were to have been coated with oil and exposed to a wind tunnel simulating Arctic conditions. Any that survived would have been killed for later autopsies.

Quite aside from the extreme localised impacts on marine mammals and birds, large oil spills in the Antarctic could cause far-reaching biological damage. Although the Southern Ocean represents only five per cent of the world's oceans in area, it accounts for 20 per cent of the total marine photosynthesis and plays a major part in deep-ocean water circulation, influencing waters far to the north. Antarctic deep-ocean water carries nutrients which feed economically important fisheries in many parts of the world — Argentine hake, Brazilian tuna, South African pilchard and the remnants of the Peruvian anchoveta fishery. Given the fragility of Antarctic marine ecosystems and our limited knowledge of them, oil disasters in Antarctic waters would be of a greater ecological magnitude than they would anywhere else, given the fragility of Antarctic marine ecosystems and our limited knowledge of them.

Oil spills would have the severest ecological consequences for two other reasons: the difficulties of salvage and clean-up operations, and the prolonged dispersal and degradation of oil under polar conditions.

The clean-up procedures for oil pollution even in the temperate oceans are woefully deficient. A recent report for an international federation of tanker owners concluded that "despite almost continuous revision of their oil pollution combat arrangements, it would appear that both governments and industry remain inadequately prepared for the future."[8] It was plain, too, said the report, that there is still no way that a large oil spill near a coast can be stopped from going ashore, and that even those clean-up methods which have been developed are rarely used effectively. Governments and industry have furthermore ignored the problems of mopping up contaminated shores and removal of the oily debris, it said.

If such is the state of the art, attempts to counter an Antarctic oil spill could only be token gestures. Even if the oil were fired, gummy residues would be left behind. Nor is it known just how long an oil spill might persist on the Southern Ocean. In the extremely cold temperatures of the Antarctic, the oil would certainly take a very long time to degrade and the more toxic constituents would take much longer to evaporate. Some biologists have estimated that if oil entered the Arctic Ocean, some of its ingredients might remain there for about 50 years.

What would happen when an oil spill became bound up in pack ice is also unknown, although preliminary tests with oil spills in the Arctic have given dramatic results. A barrel of crude oil was emptied onto the ice; within a fortnight it had

Emperor penguins guard their assembled chicks. Successive studies have found seabirds to be the most vulnerable to oil slicks and spills. An estimated 100,000 seabirds died in an oil spill in the Baltic Sea in early 1981, with most of the birds freezing to death from coated plumages. In extreme polar conditions, oil takes very much longer to degrade; additionally, Antarctica's remoteness would preclude any effective rescue or clean-up operations. *Antarctic Division, DSIR*

seeped through microscopic cracks to discolour over 1,800 cubic metres of ice. Oil trapped beneath sea ice would be frozen into the bottom of the ice and then gradually work its way to the surface through ablation and the freezing of further ice onto the bottom. A very large spill in pack ice could change its heat balance, conceivably altering the sea/ice ratio and decreasing albedo. As the pack ice is a major dynamic in climate, such an event could have very far-reaching consequences.

In considering these frightening scenarios it should be remembered that oil extraction off Antarctica's coasts would also involve the steady contamination of marine and shore ecosystems by the chronic oil releases which result from the merely routine operations of drilling rigs. There are the hazards of tanker loading, and the incidental release of one barrel of water for every barrel of oil taken. This water, known as formation water, contains about 30 parts per million of oil, made up from the oil's most toxic and water-soluble components. Even very high dilutions are harmful to marine life: a mere one part per million has been found to cause a 40 per cent mortality rate in the eggs of certain fish species. [9]

Another offshore resource has aroused considerable interest but would at least cause less environmental havoc and international tension. This is the use of Antarctic icebergs for fresh water. About 90 per cent of the world's fresh water is wrapped up in Antarctic ice, and in the 1970s the news that the ice cap discarded an estimated 350 tonnes of ice per year for each human being on the planet caught the imagination of a number of scientists and engineers, and even a Saudi prince. There seems only one historical precedent for the commercial use of an iceberg. Sailing ships at the turn of the century towed an errant berg into the Peruvian port of Callao, where it was used as ice.

Initial studies showed that the costs of obtaining fresh water from icebergs towed to arid regions would be very competitive with those of sea water desalination, the expensive technique now in use in some Middle East countries. A study by a French engineering consortium, CICERO, for the Saudi Prince Mohamed Al Faisal in 1976 revealed that it would be economically and technically feasible to tow tabular bergs of a size 11 kilometres by three kilometres to deep-water moorings off the coasts of Australia, Arabia, California, Peru or Chile.

However, feasible does not mean practicable. Like wings for pigs, iceberg exploitation has received little hard-headed research, and the technology required is scarcely at the design stage. Ocean currents would aid in the transport of bergs from off the Amery Ice Shelf to Western and South Australia, or from the Ross Ice Shelf to the Atacama Desert in Chile, in the same way that icebergs have drifted into New Zealand waters in historic times. In October 1892, the captain of the *Star of England* reported: "The morning after leaving Lyttelton, New Zealand, saw huge iceberg, a little later engines had to be stopped; completely surrounded by icebergs. Nothing but ice 300 feet high could be seen from aloft. Cleared this away during the afternoon ..." Other ships also reported seeing enormous icebergs about 400 kilometres east of New Zealand, around latitude 46°S, in the same month. Another iceberg reached the South Otago coast in 1931. [10]

But icebergs have an enormous drag, and towing them at the projected speed of two kilometres per hour would demand extremely powerful tugs and a prodigious amount of fuel. In 1966 three icebreakers in McMurdo Sound took 12 hours to push a small berg a distance of four kilometres — a speed of only 0.33 kilometres per hour. In transport to northern waters icebergs would suffer considerable wave erosion and, with their internal structures under great stress from the buffeting of waves, would be prone to fracture. Bergs waste very quickly in ocean waters above 5°C,

A one and a half million-tonne iceberg, nicknamed "Moby Dick", drifted down McMurdo Sound's shipping channel in the early 1960s and had to be forcibly ejected by the US Navy icebreaker *Atka*. Outweighed by the iceberg by about 250 to one, the *Atka* struggled for some two hours before finally pushing the berg out to sea. Although not designed for such unforeseen duties, the experience of the *Atka* exemplified the enormous practical difficulties involved in attempts to move icebergs over any distances. *Official US Navy photograph*

and if they were to be towed across the equator they would need to be somehow insulated against severe melting from the tropical sun.

There would be further problems once an average berg had been brought as close to a coast as its 200-metre draught would allow. An elaborate pipeline and pumping system would be required to tap the ice and bring it ashore as fresh water. A large iceberg off a hot and arid coast would act as a powerful air conditioner during on-shore breezes and would appreciably cool the surrounding waters over a large area. More importantly, ice floes fragmented from the main berg would constitute a hazard to shipping, particularly in the Persian Gulf with its very busy oil tanker lanes.

In view of these difficulties, the Saudi enthusiasm has now cooled somewhat. CICERO, too, has since gone bankrupt. An investigation held at the Scott Polar Research Institute at Cambridge on icebergs concluded in 1980 that their exploitation is indeed a long way off.

Deep-sea manganese nodules are another Antarctic marine possibility. The American research ship *Eltanin* discovered that extensive areas of the sea floor south of latitude 60°S had a scattering covering of "manganese" nodules. The nodules are of interest more for their high content of copper, nickel and cobalt than for the manganese. They have been the focus of attention in negotiations over mineral exploitation of the sea floor at the United Nations Law of the Sea Conference, but harvesting them is an expensive and highly technical undertaking, beyond the expertise or pocket of any country except the United States.

Sea floor mining for manganese nodules west of Acapulco, Mexico, is in the advanced planning stages, but it has been found that the valuable metal content of manganese nodules declines progressively with distance from the equator. Those on the Antarctic sea bed are thought to be much less valuable than nodules found elsewhere, so it can safely be said that the Antarctic nodules will remain unexploited for a long time to come.

On the Antarctic landmass itself, evidence of extensive mineral resources has so far been largely circumstantial.

While some preliminary "scientific" surveys are now being undertaken, there is still no indication that any mineral will be found in economic quantities, given the enormous expense of extraction in such a formidable environment.

The main circumstantial evidence that considerable mineral reserves may be found in Antarctica originates in the continent's geological affinity and primeval proximity to the Gondwana continents of Africa, South America and Australasia. But while as three continents are well known for their mineral riches, extrapolation to Antarctica can only be speculative. It has been presumed, for instance, that the mountains of the Antarctic Peninsula would bear copper as do the kindred Andes, although Chile's copper comes only from the north and central Andes (the south is practically barren).

The United States Geological Survey in 1974 was not optimistic about the chances of discovering worthwhile mineral deposits on the Antarctic continent. The survey states that the best discovery probability in any part of Antarctica is in the mountains of the peninsula, where the chances are estimated to be 0.075 (75 chances in 1,000). It is possible that the Dufek Massif is also

The terminus of the Upper Wright Glacier at the head of the dry Wright Valley. The dry valley region is virtually the only area in the world where ice and sandy desert are right next to each other. Scientists call Antarctica "a cold desert", and snowfall over much of its expanse amounts to less precipitation than occurs in many more temperate deserts. *Antarctic Division, DSIR*

highly mineralised, as its complicated geological structure is similar to some of the most productive mineral regions in the world. The Sudbury region of Ontario and the Stillwater formation in Montana, for instance, have yielded important deposits of platinum, nickel, copper and chromium; the Bushveld complex in South Africa also has these and produces lead, zinc, vanadium, iron, cobalt, tin and gold as well. But in Antarctica only coal and iron have been found in any sizable concentration, though geologists are exploring further.

Coal deposits are known at many places around the perimeter of East Antarctica and they caused quite some excitement when first noted by Shackleton's scientists in 1908. They enthusiastically estimated a "most conservative" 1.25 billion tonnes, assuming that a four-metre seam of coal extended 250,000 square kilometres into the Transantarctic Mountains. As it happens, the coal occurs in thin seams, well inland, and has never been an economic proposition even for the local supply of Antarctic bases. The deposits have a high ash content of between eight per cent and 20 per cent and are low in volatiles. This makes them worthless for coking and gasification. Transantarctic coal should thus remain undisturbed in its vast fields for centuries to come.

Potentially mineable iron ore is known in the Prince Charles Mountains, where a 100-metre thick deposit may extend for 120 kilometres. This one body has been estimated to be large enough to meet present world consumption for the next 200 years. But vast deposits, equal or much better in quality and far more accessible, exist in Australia, the Soviet Union, Canada and elsewhere. The iron content has been evaluated at only about 35-38 per cent; Australian iron ore is, in comparison, about 62-65 per cent iron.

Only a very large mineral deposit, or an extremely valuable one, could be considered. Thus deposits of chromium and platinum would attract interest as they are relatively scarce worldwide. However, the processing of chromite ores would be both very difficult and highly energy intensive, and would be uncompetitive with current sources. As for platinum, only traces of it have been discovered in Antarctica so far.

Even a rich deposit of gold might prove uneconomic to exploit unless it was readily accessible.

But one can never be too certain about what value particular minerals may be accorded in the future. It has, for example, already appeared worthwhile to fly uranium ore from Namibia, in southern Africa, to England. The Americans have been very keen in their "scientific" appraisals of the uranium potential of Antarctica, devoting many flying hours in their research programmes to "aeromagnetic surveys" and "radiometric surveys" over the Transantarctic Mountains. But uranium, in the form of eucenite, has been officially recorded only once, on the East Antarctic coast near Syowa Station. However, some scientists believe that not all finds have found their way into Antarctic literature.

SCAR's specialist committee on the potential and the problems of Antarctic mineral exploitation has reported: "No mineral deposits which are likely to be of economic value in the foreseeable future are known in Antarctica." [11] The SCAR specialists note that copper on the Antarctic Peninsula would be the best prospect, but economic feasibility studies made in 1976 by the Institute of Polar Studies at the Ohio State University indicate that Antarctic copper production would be 1.2 times as costly as buying copper on the open market. However their calculations did not include the substantial costs of transport to the appropriate market.

The problems which would face Antarctic minerals exploitation are manifold. Commercial mineral activity on the continent would need to contend with many hazards and difficulties, and would constitute a dire threat to the very simple and very fragile land ecosystems. Port installations for the export of minerals, once they had somehow been transported overland, would also be ruinous for the coastal ecologies.

If minerals were exploited onshore in the Antarctic it is likely that, as elsewhere in the world, they would also need to be enriched before being transported from the mining area. With polar transport costs the highest in the world, this would undoubtedly be the case in Antarctica. However, enrichment processing is extremely energy intensive and would demand substantial installations and a correspondingly large labour force. Large volumes of water would also be necessary, requiring further energy to melt ice and keep it liquid.

Extensive local pollution would be caused by the mining or quarrying of hardrock mineral resources on land. This would be especially so for minerals like iron, which produce large volumes of spoil. Such mining, together with the quarrying of construction materials would release large amounts of dust, contaminate drainage with metal salts and produce tailings or waste heaps with high concentrations of toxic metals.

The primary impacts of land-based mineral development would, in the main, be geographically restricted, but they would not be insignificant for that reason. Dust from mining or quarrying operations would settle over adjacent inland ice, altering its albedo and causing at least some degree of melting. The American expe-

For all but the longest transcontinental journeys, helicopters are the mainstay of polar air transport; here a Huey helicopter is parked on the summit of the Brown Peninsula in McMurdo Sound and shows, says the photographer, "a fantastic lack of unity with the dramatic backdrop of the Royal Society Range". *Mike Bradstock*

rience at McMurdo suggests strongly that changes in ice and snow cover which stem from human interference may be irreversible.

The melting of ice on the coast could conceivably be sufficient to alter the critical sea/ice balance of coastal ice shelves and the dumping of fine rock tailings into the sea could have effects which go far beyond Antarctica. The natural input of sediments into the Antarctic seas is at present considered to be slight, but because Antarctic deep-ocean water feeds all the world's oceans, the potential impact could be global. Any fuel burned in mining operations would cause long-range air pollution, detracting from Antarctica's scientific value and further interfering with albedo.

Areas of Antarctic land damaged by mineral exploration and exploitation could not be restored in the same way that they have in the Arctic, where soil fertilisation and the sowing of seeds of flowering plants have been carried out. Antarctica has only two such plant species, both confined to the northern tip of the peninsula. They are unlikely to be suited to cultivation in this way, and the introduction of alien species would contravene conservation agreements. The mosses and lichens of coastal areas are equally unsuited to propagation — the imprint of a boot in the moss beds may remain there for decades because the mosses grow no faster than one millimetre per year. Once disturbed the landscape would therefore take an extremely long time to revegetate. The most that could be done to restore land sites scarred by mineral exploitation would be to remove all equipment and imported debris and shape any disturbed land in such a way as to favour the remarkably slow process of natural colonisation.

It can be seen then that the damage and despoilation that the ecosystem would sustain with such commercial exploitation would far outweigh the dubious economic benefits to be realised.

In the Russian Arctic, mining operations have had a heavy and ugly impact on the permafrost and ice environment, but the Russians keep very quiet about them. Happily, such mining would seem most unlikely in Antarctica, at least as far as this century is concerned.

NOTES

1. *Economist*, 1 Nov 80.
2. *Press*, 21 Nov 80.
3. M. Holdgate and J. Tinker, *The Bellagio Report*, 1979.
4. *New Scientist*, 24 Jan 80.
5. *Macleans* (Canada), 21 July 80.
6. *Polar Geography*, Vol.3, p.9, 1979 (Soviet Antarctic Expedition reports).
7. Reported in *Macleans*, 21 July 80.
8. International Tanker Owner's Federation Pollution report to the Commission of European Communities, 1980.
9. *Not Man Apart*, Vol.9, No.9, Aug 1979.
10. *New Zealand Journal of Marine and Freshwater Research* 5: 80-85, 1971. See also C.J. Burrows, "Icebergs in the Southern Ocean", *New Zealand Geographer* 32:127-138, Oct 1976.
11. J.H. Zumberge, (ed.), "Possible Environmental Effects of Mineral Exploration and Exploitation in Antarctica", SCAR Report, 1979, p.4.

Chapter 9

ANTARCTICA AT THE TURNING POINT

The Antarctic "problem" has arisen from changing attitudes towards the continent. Until the early 1970s, Antarctica was seen as a scientific reserve of little economic significance. But with new pressures in the global economy since then — pressures for food, for oil and minerals, and with technological advances making access to Antarctica easier, the perspective has changed.

World commodity prices will play a big part in determining if and when oil extraction in the Antarctic goes ahead. However, as British polar authority and former Foreign Office spokesman Brian Roberts has suggested, "What we have to face in the Antarctic is not the immediate development of mineral resources but steadily increasing pressures from oil companies wishing to secure options now for use in the future." [1]

"The enormous capital investment in the present system is what we're working against," adds Dr Peter Barrett, director of Victoria University's Antarctic Research Centre in Wellington. "Against this, the expenses of exploiting Antarctic oil are only relative. With the need for oil, the stability of our political system is at stake.

"Some are saying that it is only pragmatic to move in on the Antarctic, but do they mean 'pragmatic' in a five-year or hundred-year sense? Because in a hundred years' time it will all seem to be unnecessary. Present world oil consumption stands at 62 million barrels a day. At this rate, Antarctica's possible oil reserves would last two and a half years for the entire world," Dr Barrett says. "We should be adapting our habits to what is sustainable in the long term.

"Antarctica should be left alone, but I also recognise that because the world is hooked on petroleum, very few people are going to listen."

Dr Barrett points out that despite technological progress, accidents do happen, and it is thus necessary to argue "the worst possible case" against Antarctic oil exploitation as a counter to the bland assurances of the oil companies. We have to be prepared for the worst possible accident, he says, because the oil companies will, in their turn, put the best possible face on Antarctic development. Damage to the polar environment would not immediately affect the people who benefit from the resources and the Treaty nations have already demonstrated in their past negotiations that environmental concerns are given the back seat when other political and economic considerations are at stake.

There is not yet any effective challenge

New Zealand's Scott Base, photographed in 1980 while construction of extensions was under way. The new powerhouse and biology laboratory can be seen behind the line of huts in the centre foreground which comprise the original base buildings established in 1957. *Antarctic Division, DSIR*

to these distorted priorities, although conservationists are at present organising an active campaign to lobby for the Antarctic cause. In the United States an international committee, the Antarctic and Southern Ocean Coalition, representing over 100 conservation groups from 20 countries, has been set up to watch over exploitation attempts in the Antarctic.

In New Zealand, environmental and peace groups such as Friends of the Earth, Greenpeace, the United Nations Association and Campaign for Nuclear Disarmament have also formed a coalition in order to lobby more effectively for the defence of the Antarctic.

Environmentalists in Australia have been particularly active and Friends of the Earth (Australia) have published a book on the legal and political background to the Antarctic controversies. They, together with Greenpeace, Project Jonah, the Marine Action Centre, the Australian Conservation Foundation and several other groups, also closely monitored the 1980

Marine Living Resources Convention in Canberra.

The Antarctic's resources have been a fundamental motive for political interest in Antarctica since the turn of the century. Certainly in the post-war era the possibility that Antarctica might some day yield valuable minerals has not been far from mind amongst the Treaty nations. In 1953 Admiral Byrd said that Antarctica was "a vast untouched reservoir of natural resources. As we recklessly squander our natural resources in this country [the United States] we will come to need these new resources. It is imperative that they do not fall into the hands of a potential enemy." [2]

By this time the Americans had discovered that their unofficial sector in Marie Byrd Land was the most unpromising region in Antarctica for mineral riches. Its coasts were virtually inaccessible and there was little bare rock: the ice sheet was found to be so thick that much of the bedrock was below sea level. Not coincidentally the United States soon after pressed for an international settlement which would allow it access to the entire continent.

American interest in Antarctica's mineral potential has been strong since the late 1960s when, under the Nixon Administration, it seemed that the United States Government "would be unwilling to take any steps which directly reduced the freedom of American companies to go where they wanted in the Antarctic and to do whatever appeared to be commercially attractive". [3] In the early 1970s, the Department of the Interior, one of the four departments in the government's Antarctic policy committee, insisted that the United States option supporting mineral exploitation be retained, while the Federal Energy Office urged that the exploitation option should be kept open "regardless of diplomatic or environmental consequences". [4]

Under the Carter Administration the United States adopted a more moderate tone. President Carter stated in 1977 that, "Because this remote, unpopulated region greatly influences the stability of the entire earth's oceans and atmosphere, its unique environment must be preserved." But United States pressure has been the chief impetus for a minerals regime. Further, under a Reagan Presidency, the United States may well be more favourable to exploitation.

The growing interest of American companies in the Antarctic comes at a time when the National Science Foundation budget has been under unsympathetic scrutiny by Congress. The soaring costs of logistical support for the United States Antarctic programme stem from the recent surge in fuel prices. For the 1979-80 season diesel fuel cost about 16 cents a litre at McMurdo; during the 1980-81 season the cost rose to around 34 cents a litre. Under duress, the National Science Foundation has been emphasising the "relevance" of Antarctic research in seeking government funds — that is, the chances for financial returns. But the United States Government has evidently decided it can no longer fully finance Antarctic research. As part of a $US700 million project to study the earth's continental margins, oil companies will be funding six holes to be drilled by the *Glomar Explorer* in the Weddell Sea in January 1984.

It has been no coincidence either that the Federal Electric Corporation, a subsidiary of the multinational International Telephone and Telegraph (ITT), should tender for, and win, the supply and maintenance contract for the American Antarctic bases in 1980. ITT have similar contracts with offshore oil concerns in the Northern Hemisphere and are apparently intent on ensuring that they establish themselves at the likely forefront of Antarctic oil exploitation. This multinational has a history of unsavoury and underhand dealings. [5] When one adds to this ITT's involvement with the CIA in the overthrow of the Allende Government in Chile, the picture of a multinational with its own ideas about world government becomes clearer. The former holder of the contract, Holmes' and Narver, was also widely rumoured to be a CIA "front" company.

Russian interest in Antarctic minerals has been clear for some time, for the Soviet Union has the largest and most explicitly resource-oriented research programme in Antarctica. Despite this, the Soviet Union has consistently opposed any exploitation of Antarctic minerals on environmental grounds. This opposition is puzzling, for the Russians have let no such scruples interfere with mining and oil production in their Arctic territories. With adequate oil reserves of their own, however, the Russians have no great political interest in facilitating American access to any prospective Antarctic oil. The Russians might also be wary of the potential damage to krill and Antarctic fish stocks from oil developments.

Japan's attitude to the question of

Insignia from the US Coast Guard, which provides ice-breaking services in the Ross Sea region. Ninety degrees South marks the point where all lines of longitude converge — that is, at the South Pole. The world's last frontier must not become the world's last gasp for resources, yet many talk as if Antarctic exploitation is an inevitable answer to global shortages. *Michael Bland*

mineral resources in Antarctica has become explicit with the extensive geophysical work being done by the *Hakurei Maru*. Almost all Japan's oil comes from the politically turbulent Middle East; negotiations for a political settlement for Antarctic oil exploration no doubt seem far less worrisome than the tenuous Middle East supply. While the Japanese seismic surveys are being undertaken by the Japan National Oil Corporation, a government agency, it is well known that the line between government and industry in Japan is highly permeable. "We see the programme as a basic survey on possible oil deposits," comments an executive of the Japanese Oil Mining Industry Federation. [6]

From Australia's defensive attitude towards its Antarctic territories only a trace of imagination is required to assess the Australian interest in polar minerals. For example, one of the seven members of Australia's Antarctic Research Policy Advisory Committee is Mr R. Woodall, the Director of Exploration for the Western Mining Corporation Ltd. Although Australia has an abundance of mineral resources and its own offshore oilfield to develop in Bass Strait, Australian anticipation of Antarctic treasures is implicit in its recharged Antarctic programme: "There is much to be done to consolidate our claims and to equip us with a credible

position when the treaty comes up for renewal." [7] A closer co-operation between Australia and New Zealand in Antarctic affairs was advocated in 1980 by New Zealand's Minister of Energy, Mr Birch. In an address to the Australasian Institute of Mining and Metallurgy, he declared: "It is vital to Australia's and New Zealand's interests as nations with long associations with Antarctica that we reach understandings on the region's mineral potential . . . with agreement between us, the rest of the world is likely to listen." [8]

So far there has been no indication of such trans-Tasman consultations eventuating and Australia and New Zealand are no closer on Antarctic matters than they are on any other regional issue. Co-ordination and co-operation in their scientific programmes over the last 25 years has been non-existent. Except for the recent arrangement whereby RAAF aircraft assist in the annual Christchurch-McMurdo airlift in return for an American ski-plane shuttle between McMurdo and Casey Stations, Antarctic contact between the two countries has been minimal.

As previously noted, New Zealand's Antarctic policy underwent considerable surgery with the change in government in 1975. Some would contend that lack of support from other Treaty nations forced the abandonment of the world park proposal, but with the strong possibility of oil being found under the sea within New Zealand's claim, it is obvious that the government was keeping an eye on the country's prospective share.

Mr Birch maintained that New Zealand was on the verge of a new era in Antarctic affairs — one that must reflect "the economic realities of sovereignty". In his speech to the Australasian miners and metallurgists, he continued: "The energy crisis in particular has made it much more likely that commercial development of Antarctica's mineral resources, especially those of the Ross Sea area, will take place in the not too distant future."

But there was no unified front within

the New Zealand Government on Antarctic policy; even Cabinet was said to be split on the whole issue of Antarctic development. Some parliamentarians, including Dr Ian Shearer, appointed Minister for the Environment in 1981, have spoken in favour of conservationist ideals, but the only recent government visitors to Antarctica have been Mr Birch and his undersecretary, Mr Brill. The Ministry of Energy has taken a keen interest in Antarctica of recent years, despatching departmental delegates to Treaty meetings. Scientists have, however, been consistently critical of the fact that scientific advisors have not been taken to the meetings and thus the departmental delegates have often been poorly informed.

Renewed interest and speculation over Antarctic resources in the last few years has put considerable pressure on the Treaty nations to shape up an internationally acceptable regime, both to legitimise their own vested national interests and to forestall any broader international initiative. Treaty diplomats and politicians have begun their negotiations from the fear of either uncontrolled exploitation or the removal of stewardship from their collective shoulders.

At the 1977 Consultative Meeting in London, the British Minister of State, Mr Ted Rowlands, spoke with some urgency on the need to conclude a satisfactory minerals regime: "If we do not face up to this challenge, a vacuum will be created, and that vacuum will be filled if not by us then by others." Although lofty pronouncements reaffirming their honourable

The South African research and supply ship *Agulhas* reflected in the waters of Polarbjorn Bay, near SANAE III. Like the Australians, the South Africans have stepped up their Antarctic activities in recent years. Similarly, their scientific presence has had more to do with foreign policy objectives than the pursuit of knowledge. Current South African scientific projects on subantarctic Marion Island, for instance, embrace "the ecology of the house mouse" and "decomposition studies". *South African Consulate*

intentions continue to issue forth from the consultative meetings, there is considerable scepticism about the ability of the Treaty states to step in if exploitation is begun either by one of their own number or by a non-member nation intent on gaining an advantage.

The momentum for a settlement was clearly established at the 1981 Consulative Meeting in Buenos Aires. The Treaty nations recommended that a mineral resources regime should be concluded "as a matter of urgency" and that a special consultative meeting be convened to that effect. But as already mentioned, the Antarctic Treaty was not designed to cope with the commercial development of the south polar regions. At the time the Treaty was drawn up a protocol was needed quickly; the likelihood of exploitation seemed remote and negotiations for it would have been too protracted. The basics of a minerals regime have more or less been agreed upon, but the fine details will be a major stumbling block. On the topic of oil exploitation, the Antarctic Treaty is as vague in defining its jurisdiction over the sea bed as it is silent on mineral issues generally.

The success of the Antarctic Treaty system, relative to other international arrangements elsewhere in the world, has rested on its avoidance of confrontation on the complicated sovereignty issue. This has enabled a spirit of co-operation for scientific endeavour which could easily be jeopardised by any further political settlement in aid of exploitation. One claimant state began the negotiations by insisting that its sovereignty be recognised before the Antarctic Treaty could be extended to include mineral resources. [9] Conflicting claims over territory just north of the Treaty area have already led to gunfire. In February 1976 an Argentine destroyer fired warning shots across the bows of the British research vessel *Shackleton*. According to the Argentinians, the British were conducting geological surveys with a view to oil exploi-

tation on the continental shelf off the sorely contested Falkland Islands. It should be remembered that Argentina's vehement claims to the peninsula area are directly related to the dispute over the Falklands.

Negotiations for a minerals regime cannot hope to resolve the sovereignty issue; they can only aim for an accommodation of the widely divergent interests of the Treaty nations. But a precedent for this already exists in the international convention for Spitzbergen, an Arctic archipelago far to the north of Norway. Like Antarctica, Spitzbergen was uninhabited when discovered by an English navigator in 1596, and it, too, has had a chequered history of scientific expeditions and marine mammal devastation. Under the Treaty of Svalbard of 1920, however, all signatories are guaranteed equal economic access to the islands, conditional on Norwegian sovereignty. The Norwegians and Russians are both engaged in mining operations on Spitzbergen — operations accompanied by suitable environmental havoc — with the Soviet Union paying production royalties to Norway.

The same sort of arrangement will form the basis for an Antarctic minerals regime. A regulatory authority will assess applications for mineral exploration and exploitation to ensure minimal assault on the Antarctic environment. For technical and scientific input, the authority will probably rely on a scientific advisory body, as does the Marine Resources Commission. The operations of approved commercial activity will be regulated by the management authority and the production royalties will be shared among the Treaty nations, with claimant states getting a larger share than non-claimants in recognition of their "economic rights". There will also be a provision that ensures some return for the world community at large.

The setting up of a management authority poses a number of unsettling questions. How will it be structured? Who will be party to its decisions? What sort of control will it be able to exert over such heavyweight commercial enterprises? Various governments have already found that multinational mineral companies tend to be less than scrupulous or trustworthy in their operations. How will the openness of Antarctic research be affected by the secrecy of commercial activity? The Bellagio Report envisaged a management authority which would "evaluate [commercial] projects of a confidential nature". [10] Confidentiality in Antarctica would be the very antithesis of the freedom of scientific investigation and information which has been the continent's greatest human asset.

Environmentalists are thus almost as disturbed about the legal and political dimensions of the evolving minerals convention as they are about the grave ecological risks the regime is supposed to regulate. Mr Birch has assured Friends of the Earth that New Zealand is pressing for "the widest possible protection to the fragile Antarctic environment" during the minerals regime negotiations. But it should be noted that in the last decade of informal discussion about a regime by the Treaty nations, they have made no moves to initiate or fund environmental research to help answer the great unknowns about Antarctic mineral exploration and exploitation. No suggestion of an internationally funded environmental research programme has received serious attention from the Treaty powers. While the convention is to make some deference to the complete lack of scientific research on the ecological consequences of Antarctic minerals development, its provisions for responding to scientific input are likely to be weak and ineffective.

For the oil industry, Antarctic oil would be a technological adventure; for the Treaty governments it amounts to a calculated risk. For concerned conservationists it promises unmitigated ruin of the Antarctic wilderness. Just as they had feared, some nations saw the Marine Living Resources Convention as just a rehearsal for the more crucial convention on non-living resources. The United States, with no financial interest of its own in Antarctic living resources, failed to assert strong conservation measures in case too strict a precedent was set for the minerals regime to follow.

The Americans compromised on the powers of the regulatory commission (it is only advisory), and on the insistence on majority rule, accepting a double veto voting system which virtually guarantees that no restrictive measures will be introduced. During the marine convention negotiations, the United States was instrumental in the withdrawal of a proposal by Chile to prohibit land-based krill and fish processing plants on the Antarctic continent. A second proposal to ban fishing within set limits off the coast was similarly opposed, again because such a measure might prejudice the future minerals regime, with its correspondence to offshore oil drilling.

New Zealand appears to be very active in the convention negotiations and has acted as an intermediary between countries with more extreme positions. Australia played a similar role in the Marine Living Resources Convention, but has been less flexible on the minerals question where much more is at stake.

The exploitation of Antarctic resources would also have a number of implications for New Zealand, which is already closely associated with the United States Antarctic Programme and would be unable to maintain Scott Base if for some reason the Americans suddenly withdrew their logistical support. The Nukey Poo reactor at McMurdo was also situated in New Zealand-claimed territory, and thousands of tonnes of radioactive soil contaminated by this nuclear white elephant were shipped through the port of Lyttelton. This episode remains perhaps the most telling symbol of the threat to New Zealand's independence which could come from development of Antarctica. Several details of this reactor's operation still remain secret: among them, the safeguards taken when disposing of the spent fuel rods and the details of the United States Navy's soil sample results.

New Zealand and Australia are likely to be seen as politically reliable staging posts for any large venture to exploit Antarctica. For instance, the link between New Zealand and West Germany is becoming very close at a time when the West Germans are establishing a large-scale Antarctic presence. West Germany bank-rolled much of New Zealand's foreign borrowing in the 1970s, and there were visits in 1979 by the West German President and a delegation of top German businessmen. Their immediate interest was no doubt focused on cheap energy supplies to be provided by the New Zealand Government for new energy-intensive industries.

However, the prospect of using New Zealand as a base for future Antarctic adventures is also likely to have some bearing on the establishment of this closer relationship between the two countries. A formal agreement, relating to mutual logistic support in Antarctica, was reached in June 1981 between the New Zealand and West German governments. Like Japan, West Germany is very much dependent on Middle East oil, and the West Germans have been the first to make intensive local geophysical surveys in the Ross Sea. A West German geological team made a 10-week expedition to Northern Victoria Land in the 1979-80 season, and the West Germans were to be a major force in the research planned for the area in the 1981-82 season. Timaru has been used by the Germans as a base for their Antarctic operations, and instructors recommended by the DSIR Antarctic Division have been involved in training German team members at Mt Cook and in Northern Victoria Land.

Whether New Zealand likes it or not, it seems bound to become more and more deeply involved in Antarctic politics. In June 1980 the Antarctic Division Superintendent, Bob Thomson, and Canterbury University zoologist, Prof George Knox, made a two-week visit to China as guests of the Chinese Government. The Chinese were seeking advice on plans for their Antarctic activities, and the two New Zealanders were impressed both by the large number of well-equipped Chinese oceanographic ships and by the zeal with which the Chinese are preparing to launch themselves into Antarctic science. "They were much further advanced than I had expected," remarked Mr Thomson in a newspaper report. "For a country with no direct links yet established in Antarctica an astonishing amount of work is already being done." [11]

As part of their more outward-looking international posture the Chinese are obviously enthusiastic about participating in Antarctic science and in the élite political club that goes with it. A national Antarctic research committee has now been set up and a permanent base on the continent — the entry ticket for the Treaty fraternity — is under consideration. The Chinese already have an oceanographic ship suitable for Antarctic work and have made offers to have New Zealand scientists on board. Two Chinese scientists attended the SCAR meeting in Queenstown

An American Starlifter on the ice at McMurdo. The United States is very dependent on New Zealand as a staging post for its Antarctic operations, just as New Zealand relies largely on American logistical support in its polar programme. With Antarctica increasingly becoming a focus of international attention, New Zealand's strategic position must be borne in mind. *Ray Goldring*

and visited the Antarctic Division head-quarters in Christchurch in 1980; further activities are planned. Co-operative research ventures between China and New Zealand would thus seem very likely in the near future, with the latter being used as a base for oceanographic research in the Antarctic.

At this stage the Chinese do not appear to be motivated by the quest for Antarctic resources. They told their New Zealand visitors that because of untapped resources closer to home, they have no interest in mineral exploration in the Antarctic. (Early in 1981 China announced the discovery of massive offshore oil fields on the northern continental shelf of the South China Sea.) Nor are the Chinese about to eye up krill, for they are still developing their coastal marine resources and have no experience of deep-sea fishing. Rather, the move into the international community by Chinese scientists reflects their frustration with decades of isolation brought on by the dramatic political upheavals within China. "Now they want to get involved in international science again, and they see the Antarctic as a place where it has worked well," adds Mr Thomson. [12]

Over the last decade, the Antarctic Treaty has come under increasing pressure from the world community, and there have been repeated calls for the opening up of Antarctic politics. But there seems no way that the Treaty members will give up their political hold on Antarctica, and calls that the continent be internationalised have caused the Treaty members only to close their ranks. At the biennial consultations, the Treaty members have consistently reaffirmed their political prerogatives in Antarctic affairs and have shown no intention of widening the Treaty to the rest of the world — save for a select few countries.

However, the Antarctic Treaty nations have been forced to acknowledge the internationalist argument to some degree. The minerals convention is to contain revenue-sharing arrangements that offer some economic benefit to the developing countries. The formula for this will be derived from the procedures decided on by the United Nations Conference on the Law of the Sea. The Conference has been a contributing factor in the accelerated pace of Antarctic Treaty consultations, for many in the world community view Antarctica as just as much a part of the global commons as the deep-sea bed with which the Conference has concerned itself. The resulting treaty, to be signed by the world's nations in 1982, governs the exploitation of the sea floor, and the Antarctic Treaty states have been anxious to parry this important milestone in international relations with a settlement of their own. The treaty contains particularly stringent measures to combat oil pollution in ice-infested areas, and the ability of the Antarctic Treaty nations to match these in their own convention remains to be seen.

Although the Antarctic Treaty is far from perfect, to place Antarctica under United Nations control could be far worse. The United Nations has too broad and divergent a constituency to govern Antarctica effectively. Additionally, the United Nations is dominated by Third World countries, which have little knowledge of the white continent but would probably be keen to exploit it. The Treaty nations have at least a nodding regard for the Antarctic environment while, understandably, the developing countries would be much more interested in extracting Antarctica's resources than in conservation. Even amongst the Treaty nations there is a sufficiently great range of interests and perspectives for there to be considerable danger of conservation ideals being overshadowed by political and economic forces — as has already happened with the Marine Living Resources Convention.

However, the Treaty procedures are much too slow to cope with the accelerating events in Antarctic affairs. Matters for formal discussion by the Treaty nations must be placed on the agenda two years ahead, and Treaty recommendations must be adopted by unanimous vote. Moreover, the recommendations do not bind the Treaty parties until approved by the governments of all consultative members. This gentlemanly pace may have been quite appropriate for the first years of the Treaty; in the 1980s it is a liability.

The Antarctic Treaty nations should give the speeding up of Treaty procedures a much higher priority, but they have been reluctant to do so. At the Washington meeting in 1979 a proposal for more meetings was rejected and instead the practice of informal intersessional meetings and special meetings on particular topics was reaffirmed.

The regulation that the marine and mineral regimes will impose on Antarctic affairs will not come into operation until the documents are ratified by a majority of Treaty nations. That this could easily amount to a lag of 10 years can be seen from the delays in ratification of other important Antarctic conventions in which economic interests are scarcely threatened. Measures for the conservation of Antarctic wildlife still await final ratification.

The Antarctic Treaty has no fixed expiry date but, as Treaty nations are well aware, it will be up for review in 1991. In the 1980s the revitalised commitment to Antarctic research evident in some countries (not New Zealand) will be viewed by cynics as a self-interested jockeying for position on the part of the Treaty nations; optimists will see it as an indication that the fragility of the Antarctic environment will be more clearly exposed and that more protective measures will be formulated.

Many Antarctic scientists are very concerned about the future scientific and environmental integrity of the Antarctic. The scientific investigation of Antarctica has been the most successful programme of international research in the history of science. However, it can only be prejudiced by commercial activity on the continent. Exploitation and its con-

sequences would also seriously impair Antarctica's role as a relatively undisturbed scientific laboratory. As a remote wilderness, Antarctica has a unique capacity to serve as a monitor for global pollution levels; its distinction as a free scientific zone could not be maintained if mineral exploitation goes ahead.

As the scientific advisory body to the Antarctic Treaty, SCAR is the only other international force in the south polar region. "SCAR is the watchdog for the scientific community," explains its president, Prof George Knox of Canterbury University.

But SCAR is in a difficult position. Although it has a greater awareness of the hazards of human activity in Antarctica, it has little political authority and some of its working groups, such as the geology group, are anxious to avoid "political questions". But because the working groups consider purely "scientific" issues, untainted by political exigencies, they can be the most effective elements of SCAR. The glaciology group, for instance, was forthright in its condemnation of the Zeller proposal to dump nuclear wastes on the Antarctic ice sheet.

"One of the things which struck me about SCAR at Queenstown [where the 1980 SCAR conference was held] was that it seemed either unwilling or unable to address the question of commercial activity," comments Dr Peter Barrett. "It really worries me that the only people who will be aware of the possibility of damage to the Antarctic environment before it happens are scientists. SCAR is the only constituency that the Antarctic has. It must not remain aloof, but it is multicultural, and thus a common ground is hard to establish."

The committee's new constitution acknowledges some of the growing concern amongst scientists within SCAR for its effectiveness as the only other political force in Antarctica. Treaty governments must now back their requests for scientific advice from SCAR with the necessary funds, and the scientists are under no obligation to accept the assignment. There can hardly be a doubt that the scientists had in mind the resource-related work they will soon be called upon to carry out.

It is apparent, however, that a great deal of Antarctica's future is decided by the Treaty nations without regard to scientific information. In discussing the 1979 Washington Treaty meeting, one New Zealand diplomat reflects: "The issues weren't scientific. It was more of a politico-legal horsetrade." Antarctic scientists have been cautioned to show restraint in their impatience with Treaty proceedings. With regard to the link between SCAR and the Treaty nations, one British diplomat advised a conference of Antarctic biologists: "It should be possible to continue this happy relationship if SCAR scientists are patient and understanding about the formidable political and legal difficulties which they are asking governments to solve. Most of these difficulties can eventually be solved under the umbrella of the Antarctic Treaty. But we must not go too fast." [13]

Lack of finance is behind the inadequate scientific representation in New Zealand's delegations to Treaty consultations. At SCAR meetings or at the technical sessions which provide the scientific contribution at Treaty meetings, scientists have often attended at their own expense rather than see New Zealand unrepresented there. And in the early stages at least, New Zealand did not include a marine scientist in its delegation to the marine resources negotiations.

As a further indication of New Zealand's financial priorities, Dr Barrett cites the Upper Hutt City Council's dispatch of two engineers overseas at a cost of over $4,000 to gather information for the proposed civic swimming pool. Yet the Government will not afford the air fare for marine scientists invited to join research ships leaving from, say, Punta Arenas. "If we're going to be fully heard we've got to be participating," remarks Prof Knox. "Opportunities have been offered under the BIOMASS programme — our scientists have been invited as observers aboard French and American ships, but no funds have been available to send them."

If New Zealand is to play its proper part in shaping the most exacting minerals regime that is humanly possible, then it must show a greater support for Antarctic science and display more self-sufficiency in its polar operations. Apart from the art of conciliation, New Zealand had nothing to contribute to the marine resources convention, and has offered just as little in a concrete way to the developing minerals regime. The country does not lack scientific personnel, but is sadly deficient in equipment. New Zealand has had no Antarctic research ship since 1970 and thus is unable to participate in the BIOMASS programme that will form the basis of the Marine Commission's scientific advice. While it is conceded that the Government did go to some effort to find $US80,000 to charter the Transglobe Expedition ship *Benjamin Bowring* for an 18-day cruise from McMurdo in early 1981, two New Zealand scientists on board still had to pay their own way so as to contribute to the International Survey of Antarctic Seabirds — a part of the BIOMASS programme.

With no suitable ships and only very limited air transport, New Zealand will be incapable of policing the stipulations of both the marine and the forthcoming minerals conventions.

It has been noted that until recently, Antarctic conservationists have been unable to mount an effective challenge to the popular brainwashing that Antarctic exploitation must inevitably proceed. There have been a good many proposals for the declaration of Antarctica as a world preserve, beginning with the Second World Conference on National Parks in 1972. The conference recommended that the Antarctic Treaty powers negotiate to establish the continent and its surroundings as the first World Park under the auspices of the United Nations. Not surprisingly, there was no reply from the Treaty states.

Environmentalist pleas for the Antarctic wilderness have had no chance of winning converts from the Treaty nations when they have argued the internationalist cause. It is becoming apparent that the Treaty nations' sovereignty claims and the exclusiveness of their club are really non-negotiable. These political realities must be accepted, and tactics adjusted, if the conservationist case for Antarctica is to be successful.

Friends of the Earth International nominated Antarctica as "an international wilderness area" at its Frankfurt meeting in 1978, but recognised the intention of the Treaty nations to establish a minerals regime when it called upon "all nations and their peoples to refrain from the commercial exploitation of the Antarctic region until it is established beyond reasonable doubt that such exploitation will have no detrimental impact on Antarctic and global ecosystems". From the evidence marshalled here, it is quite unlikely that such proof could ever be established.

A conservation strategy that takes into account the Antarctic's political non-negotiables has been developed by Friends of the Earth in Australia. [14] Based on the United Nations' Convention for the Protection of World Cultural and Natural Heritage, the strategy is a workable blueprint aimed at individual Treaty governments.

The World Heritage Convention in no way impinges on issues of sovereignty. It was adopted unanimously at the UNESCO General Conference in 1972, and came into force in December 1975. Under the convention, now subscribed to by about one-third of the world's nations, each state party nominates worthy areas within its territory for preservation and protection, and is obliged to make its own moves to effect the same. Guidelines were drawn up at the World Heritage Committee's first meeting, and it is interesting to examine these in some detail, for their prescriptions for natural heritage properties of "outstanding universal value" sound rather familiar.

Natural heritage properties should, according to the guidelines:

1. Be outstanding examples of the major stages of the earth's evolutionary history, including sites illustrating major epochs of geological history, such as the ice ages . . . .
2. Be outstanding examples of significant and continuing geological processes and biological evolution . . . .
3. Contain unique, rare or superlative natural phenomena, formations or areas of exceptional natural beauty. . . .
4. Be habitats for rare or endangered species of plants and animals, including areas where concentrations of plants and animals of universal interest and significance are found . . . .

Australia has ratified the World Heritage Convention and New Zealand has it under consideration. Even at this late stage New Zealand and Australia could act to make their Antarctic claims "national parks" to be safeguarded from all commercial activity. The Ross Dependency and the Australian Antarctic Territories should be promulgated by respective governments as natural heritage reserves, and be added to the World Heritage list. Other claimants could be encouraged to do the same; if not now, then when the Treaty comes up for review in 1991 — when the sovereignty issue is bound to be aired again. The sooner a claimant state sets the precedent, however, the better.

By urging such a move now, conservationists can, over the next decade, establish a momentum towards the realisation in Antarctica of the aims of the World Heritage Convention. Actual commercial exploitation of the Antarctic is not expected before 1990. The continent is not yet a major source of revenue for any country, and so it would be easier now, rather than in 1991, to get governmental agreement on the preservation of Antarctica, or at least the Australasian sectors, as a wilderness under the Convention.

Some scientists in New Zealand have been unhappy about the Government's shift away from the world park concept put forward by New Zealand in 1975. They maintain that while it might seem "unrealistic" in the face of commercial pressures, New Zealand should be taking a stand. They have even pointed out that New Zealand's own interests could benefit, because pollution resulting from Antarctic exploitation, particularly of oil, would affect New Zealand more than any other country because of its geographical proximity. In fact, New Zealand's maritime zone extends almost to the edge of the Antarctic.

Unless a country is prepared to take a stand on principle, as New Zealand has been known to do in the past, the dictates of political and economic "reality" will always result in essentially the continued victory of destructive economic forces over valuable environmental integrity. The head of the United Nations Environment Secretariat, Dr Mostafal Tolba, recently warned the world that humankind is in imminent danger of polluting itself off the face of the earth. He stressed the need for a more austere lifestyle among rich people, and expressed exasperation at what he called "the continued irresponsible use of oil, coal and other non-renewable and pollutant energy sources". [15]

The unique Antarctic environment is one which must be protected. It is too fragile to withstand much interference, and compromise of the principles of stewardship by political and economic interests will inevitably lead to the sort of disaster that has occurred so often in the exploitation and shipping of oil in other parts of the world.

Contrary to the pronouncements of New Zealand's Minister of Energy, we should not see ourselves on the verge of a new era in Antarctica's history. Certainly, the shortage of resources in the future will have to be faced, but Antarctica is not the answer. We should be prepared, rather, to acknowledge the end of the world era of meat-axe technologies and industrial economies based on cheap and accessible resources and energy. Antarctica plays too vital a part in the global environment to risk tampering with.

The New Zealand and Australian Governments would be setting a moral example by declaring their Antarctic claims as nature reserves which are rightfully part of the world heritage. As one of the original American environmentalists, Henry David Thoreau, observed: "In wilderness is the preservation of the world."

NOTES

1. Brian Roberts, *Polar Record*, May 1978, p.121.
2. Quoted in Owen Wilkes' "Antarctica Up For Grabs?", *New Zealand Monthly Review*, Sept 1974.
3. Unpublished memorandum cited in *Foreign Policy* No.35, Summer 1979, p.139.
4. *New York Times*, Mar 1974, quoted in Wilkes (2) above.
5. Anthony Sampson has documented this multinational's unsavoury history in *The Sovereign State: A Secret History of ITT*, 1973. In 1977 ITT received $US27 million from the American Government for bomb damage to its German factories in World War II, including $US5 million for damage to Focke-Wulf aircraft plants, "on the basis that they were American property bombed by Allied bombers. It was a notable reward for a company that had so deliberately invested in the German war effort. . . ." (Sampson, pp. 40, 47).
6. *New Zealand Herald*, 27 Nov 80.
7. *Bulletin*, 18 March 80.
8. *Press*, 9 May 80.
9. Brian Roberts in (1) above. Roberts does not name which claimant state.
10. M. Holdgate and J. Tinker, "Oil and Mineral Prospects in Antarctica", *The Bellagio Report*, 1979, p.38.
11. *New Zealand Herald*, 21 July 80.
12. *National Business Review*, 24 Nov 80.
13. See M. Holdgate *Antarctic Ecology*, Vol.2, 1970, p.949.
14. The strategy is set out in Dr Keith Suter's *Antarctica: World Law and the Last Wilderness*, 1980.
15. *Evening Post*, 13 Sept 79.

EPILOGUE

Over the next few years world attention will be focused on the Antarctic continent as never before, as the Treaty nations hammer out a key to Pandora's lock on Antarctica's mineral potential. As this book went to press, it became known that formal deliberations for a minerals regime were set to begin in Wellington, New Zealand, in May 1982.

Like all previous Treaty negotiations, these will be held in secret: no official records will be kept, no observers permitted, and the communiques issued at the end of each session will give little insight into what has been discussed. We are told that the regime's prime purpose will be to establish a system for assessing the acceptability of potential minerals exploitation in Antarctica, and to govern any ventures that are approved. The problem will be that in the dim light of our present understanding of how the Antarctic ecosystem "works", we are quite unable to say just by what standard "acceptability" might be judged.

There is no doubt, as New Zealand's Dr Shearer has stated, that "Science itself holds the key to adequate environmental policies", or that the future of Antarctica will depend on "our capacity to use scientific method and scientific knowledge in our collective management of the continent's resources". [1] But from what sources will this scientific input spring? A provisional analysis of the pending negotiations prepared by the U.S. Department of State naively suggests that it should rest with the developers: "Thus, incentives would exist for [them] to fund research that would fill important data deficiencies so that an intelligent environmental assessment could be achieved." Such Simple Simon trust in the integrity of the American oil industry is typical of the Reagan Administration.

The environmentalists' plea for a complete moratorium on Antarctic development may have been lost for the meantime, given the transparently hard-line attitudes of the United States, Australia and New Zealand, amongst others. (The U.S. Government has countered the preservationist cause with such official dross as: "In an era when people are concerned about shortages of natural resources, it would seem impractical to attempt to set aside an antarctic [sic] preserve outside of the ambit of natural resource activity."[2]) But the opportunity still remains for the negotiation of at least a temporary moratorium. And given its repeated assertions of an intent to press for "the widest possible protection of the Antarctic continent", and as host to the Convention negotiations, New Zealand should be in a strong position to press for such a compromise.

The political problems facing the establishment of any international accord are nevertheless formidable — even at this stage, when no known resources are at stake. Although a large find of platinum with possible commercial interest is apparently to be announced around the time of the negotiations, there have been no oil discoveries to rekindle conflict over territorial claims. Moreover, political problems are in turn likely to overshadow scientific problems — including those we may not yet be aware of.

Dr Peter Barrett has pointed out that what are of greatest concern in Antarctica are not the problems we know, but those we do not know. Only five years ago it seemed impossible that global consumption of fossil fuels might bring about the collapse of the West Antarctic Ice Sheet in 100 years or so through the rise in carbon dioxide levels. Now, however, the suggestion is frighteningly real.

In response to the enormous estimate of Antarctica's oil potential made by Gulf Oil, and to those who would seek to tap it, Dr Barrett wisely states: "It still represents less than three years' supply for the world, at the present rate of production. We have to ask: Is it worth the risk?"

1. Speech at ICUN Conference, 14 Oct. 1981
2. Draft Environmental Impact Statement, July 1981.

GLOSSARY

ablation: the direct evaporation of snow and ice without a liquid phase.

albedo: the solar reflectivity of a surface.

baleen whales: the class of whales which feed by straining plankton from large mouthfuls of water.

bioluminescence: the term for the light that some living organisms (e.g. glow-worms) can make for themselves.

BIOMASS: a current Antarctic research programme, coined from Biological Investigation Of Marine Antarctic Systems and Stocks. Biomass is also a scientific term for the total weight of all living matter in a certain volume of material (e.g. sea water).

EEZ: the common abbreviation for Exclusive Economic Zone, as applied to marine territory.

FAO: the United Nations Food and Agriculture Organisation.

Gondwana: the original southern supercontinent, composed of Africa, South America, Antarctica, Australasia and the Indian subcontinent.

igneous: derived from a molten state.

IGY: International Geophysical Year, which marked 18 months of unprecedented international scientific research and co-operation during 1957-58.

ionosphere: the envelope of ionised particles which surrounds the earth and cushions it from the bombardment of cosmic rays.

isostasy: the geological principle that the earth's crust has a certain buoyancy against its molten interior, analagous to a raft on a lake.

isotherms: a measurement of climate, being lines that connect places which have the same mean annual temperature.

isotopes: variant forms of an element, differing in atomic weight but with the same chemical properties.

IWC: the International Whaling Commission.

katabatic winds: winds resulting from a downward flow of cold air.

orogen: a folding of the earth's crust; an area affected by a particular phase of mountain building.

plankton: tiny animals and plants which float in seas, rivers and lakes at the mercy of currents.

SCAR: the Scientific Committee on Antarctic Research.

SCOR: the Scientific Committee on Oceanographic Research.

REFERENCES

Because Antarctica is very much a topical issue, the writing of this book entailed extensive reference to a broad range of newspaper reports and magazine articles, unpublished memoranda and scientific papers, many of which have been footnoted in the text. Material was also garnered from conversations with a dozen or so individuals professionally concerned with the Antarctic. For brevity's sake, only major references are listed here.

Auburn F.M., *The Ross Dependency*, The Hague, 1972

Beeby, Christopher, *The Antarctic Treaty*, Wellington 1972

Bengtson, John L., *Review of Information Regarding The Conservation of Living Resources of the Antarctic Marine Ecosystem, Final Report to US Marine Mammal Commission*, Washington, 1978

Central Intelligence Agency, *Polar Regions Atlas*, Washington, 1978

Christie E.W.H., *The Antarctic Problem*, London, 1951

Department of State (US), *Final Environmental Impact Statement for a Possible Regime for Conservation of Antarctic Living Marine Resources*, Washington, 1978

Earthscan, *Antarctica and Its Resources*, London, 1980

Everson, Inigo, *The Living Resources of the Southern Ocean*, FAO, Rome, 1977

Finkel, George, *Antarctica, the Heroic Age*, Sydney, 1976

Hatherton, Trevor (ed.), *Antarctica*, Wellington, 1965

Holdgate, Martin, *Antarctic Ecology* (2 vols), London, 1970

Holdgate, Martin and Tinker, Jon, "Oil and Other Minerals in Antarctica", *The Bellagio Report*, SCAR, Cambridge, 1979

Huntford, Roland, *Scott and Amundsen*, London, 1979

Institute of Polar Studies, *A Framework for Assessing Environmental Impacts of Possible Antarctic Mineral Development*, Ohio State University, 1977

King H.E.R., *The Antarctic*, London, 1969

Lewis, R.S. and Smith, P.M. (eds.), *Frozen Future: A Prophetic Report From Antarctica*, New York, 1973

Logan, H.F.M., *Cold Commitment — New Zealand and the Ross Dependency*, Canterbury University Thesis, Christchurch, 1978

Lovering, J.F. and Prescott, J.R.V., *Last of Lands . . . Antarctica*, Melbourne, 1979

Mitchell, Barbara, and Sandbrook, Richard, *The Management of the Southern Ocean*, International Institute for Environment and Development, London, 1980

Parker, Bruce (ed.), *Conservation in Antarctica: Proceedings of a Colloquium*, Blacksburg, Virginia, 1970

Parker, Bruce (ed.), *Environmental Impact in Antarctica*, Blacksburg, Virginia, 1978

Price, Grenfell, *The Winning of Australian Antarctica*, Sydney, 1962

Quartermain, L.B., *South to the Pole*, Wellington, 1967

Quartermain, L.B., *New Zealand and the Antarctic*, Wellington, 1971

Suter, Keith, *Antarctica: World Law and the Last Wilderness*, Friends of the Earth, Sydney, 1980

Turner, Maurice, *Ten Years in Tierra Del Fuego*, Melbourne, 1981

Wright, N.A. and Williams, P.L., *Mineral Resources of Antarctica*, US Geological Survey Circular 705, Washington, 1974

Zumberge, J.H., "Mineral Resources and Geopolitics in Antarctica," *American Scientist*, January 1979

Zumberge, J.H. (ed.), *Possible Environmental Effects of Mineral Exploitation and Exploitation in Antarctica* — SCAR, Cambridge, 1979

INDEX